Being Old is Different

Being Old
is
Different

Person-centred care for old people

Marlis Pörtner

PCCS BOOKS
Ross-on-Wye

PCCS BOOKS
2 Cropper Row
Alton Road
ROSS-ON-WYE
HR9 5LA
UK
Tel +44 (0)1989 763900

www.pccs-books.co.uk

This edition published 2008

First published as
Pörtner, M *Alt sein ist anders. Personzentrierte Betreuung von alten Menschen.*
Klett-Cotta
© 2005, J.G. Cotta'sche Buchhandlung Nachfolger GmbH
Stuttgart

For the English language translation:
© 2008, Marlis Pörtner

Being Old is Different
Person-centred care for old people

ISBN 978-1-898-05999-8

Cover design by Old Dog Graphics
Printed by Cpod, Trowbridge, UK

Contents

Acknowledgments

I wish to offer a warm thank you to all the people who, directly or indirectly, have contributed to the creation of this book by working with me, or sharing ideas and experiences; particularly to those colleagues who are committed to spreading my ideas by training and consulting staff and institutions. Once more I am grateful to my German publishers Klett-Cotta, particularly Dr. Heinz Beyer, for consistent and agreeable cooperation. My sincere thanks to PCCS Books, particularly to Maggie Taylor-Sanders and Pete Sanders for making this English edition possible, to Pete particularly for his helpful advice with some difficult parts of the translation. Last, but not least, a special thank you to Helen Dean for competent and sensitive editing of the English text.

Staufen, Switzerland, January 2008
Marlis Pörtner

Introduction

Why is it different to be old? Different from what and in what way?

Being old is different in many ways: different from what we anticipated when we were younger, different from other chapters in our lives, different for each person and different from times past. The concept of old age has dramatically changed during the last fifty years and so have the opportunities for old people; demographic and social developments will inevitably cause further, as yet unforeseeable, changes. We are now in the middle of this transformation process and our concepts of old age are shaped by traditional images as well as by new perspectives that are opening up.

Being old is not what the (old and new) clichés suggest. The illusory image of the 'young elderly', left nearly untouched by the years, feeling as fit as ever and apparently unable to detect any sign of old age (becoming slower, more forgetful, losing interest in things that used to be important, etc.) is as inadequate as the opposite cliché that presents old people as frail, a little 'gaga', not to be taken too seriously, not up to date and constantly in need of patronising advice. However, like any clichés, these bear a grain of truth. Being old fluctuates somewhere between these extremes; it contains traces of both and, above all, is a totally new and individual experience, unique and different for each person. To look at the complexity of these differences is the aim of this book.

At first, when certain people tried to talk me into writing a book on person-centred care for old people, I hesitated. It didn't seem necessary; several examples in my book *Trust and Understanding* (Pörtner, 1996, 2000, 2007) demonstrate how, with some modifications, the principles and guidelines described there are just as valuable in the care of old people as for people 'with special needs'.

Nevertheless, the more I thought about it, the more I became tempted. In the context of old age, there are some new and specific aspects to consider. Of course, the basic person-centred principles of care are the same, but the themes of life are different, and they affect carers too since, some day, those themes will be theirs. The daily routine of caring for people in the last chapter of their lives has another perspective than caring for people with disabilities who need support in coping with daily life and in developing, as much as possible, their limited capabilities. But people with disabilities are ageing too, so consideration will be given to this in the last chapter of this book.

The particular issue of people with dementia will not be dealt with in a separate chapter but embedded in general considerations about what is essential in the care of old people as, in my view, a person with dementia also has a right to be seen and understood as a whole person. There is a fluid border between 'normal' impairments due to old age and those caused by dementia, and they can be considerably influenced by the quality of care.

This book is not about specific nursing or therapy methods but about fundamental principles, valuable in different areas of care. The term 'carer', therefore, is used here for all those who, professionally or voluntarily, work with old people, and the term 'care' embraces nursing as well as therapeutic and supportive activities. The female and male forms are used alternately.

Some basic person-centred principles and their implementation in everyday care will be described; the themes that become relevant in the last chapters of life, and their impact on care for old people, will be highlighted. The book will aim to demonstrate why the person-centred approach is particularly useful in this field; how it can be transferred into practice; how it helps to improve the life quality of old people and, at the same time, makes work more satisfying for carers.

The common ground on which both books are based has resulted in some overlapping with *Trust and Understanding*, from where I have deliberately transferred a few examples that make particularly clear what is essential in person-centred care for old people.

Being old myself, I was, beyond professional interest, also challenged on a personal level to think over this aspect of my existence. Therefore, a few personal considerations will get readers in the mood for the subject.

1
Growing old is a strange experience: some personal considerations

Why is it strange to grow old? Isn't it a quite natural experience that all human beings—except those who die young—have in common? Ageing begins at birth and ends with death. We are in this process all our lives and we experience it differently at different ages. As children, getting older is never quick enough for us, we long to be ten or twelve or sixteen or twenty and can't wait for it to happen. Later on, conversely, time goes by at a frightening tempo, slipping through our fingers, and we wish sometimes that we could stop, or at least slow it down a little.

When are we 'old'? At sixty, seventy, or eighty? It depends on our perspective. When I was twenty, in the little theatre group I belonged to at the time, there was a 'very old' colleague (in our estimation) with whom 'nevertheless' we were on excellent terms—she was actually forty! Nowadays, the forty-year-olds, to me, are young people. But, even though the concept 'old' is relative, it is not to be disputed or denied: some day we really will be old. We know it, and we also know that we should think about it in time. And we believe—as long as it is still far away—that we will be well prepared for it and certainly able to handle it better than some old people around us who, in our eyes, have difficulty accepting their age. Well, we certainly know *that* we will be old some day but we don't know anything about *how* this will be for us. We might have some ideas about it but once the time has come, everything is different.

In younger years, I was sure that I would know exactly what to do later and how to handle things. I would certainly not miss the right moment to retire but, in time (at around sixty I thought), I would consider moving to an old people's residence. I would certainly not make the same mistakes as my mother who, late in her eighties, still didn't realise she was old and would have to make some changes to her life, even though it was obvious that she couldn't continue in the same way. But, strangely enough, the older I got the more the idea receded into the distance. Now I am in my seventies and certainly not planning to move to a residential home—far from it, I am quite determined to avoid it if at all possible. I don't feel that life is somehow over and that it is time for me to withdraw. On the contrary, I see new perspectives opening up in these late years. Despite some aches and pains, I experience this chapter of life not primarily as decline but as a period of transformation in which values change, new horizons appear and the focus shifts.

Of course, the latter years are also a time of loss and grief: people close to us die, things once meaningful are not possible anymore, or no longer of importance. The saying that 'we must let go' becomes very real. And each letting go means the end of something that, before, had been part of life and important. Yet, at the same time, a space is opening for something new to evolve; something unknown and never dreamt of. Letting go means not only loss but also liberation. Sometimes it's the loss we feel most intensely, at other times the freedom. There are lighter and darker days in old age—just as in any other chapter of life.

What exactly does 'old' mean? 'We are "elder" not old', a friend of my age used to say, correcting me when I referred to us as 'old ladies'. She is not the only one to see it that way. Only recently, an official who probably meant to be polite, addressed me as 'being in higher middle-age!' The tendency to avoid the word 'old', as if it were an insult, is widespread. People talk about the 'elderly' instead, or about 'senior citizens', which seems to be considered less insulting. Sometimes the ominous word 'old' is avoided in a way that makes it hard to understand what the person actually wants to say. An assistant in a chemist's shop, recommending a face-cream 'for demanding skin', struggles to contain her composure when I ask her: 'Does that mean for old ladies?' I have no problem when my doctor finds that 'for my age' I am in good shape, while others my age would consider it an insult.

Personally, I consider it insulting to avoid or circumscribe the word 'old' as if it were shameful to be old. Why is 'old' such a taboo? It means nothing more than that a person has lived for a considerable number of years and is now in the latter part of her life. It doesn't say anything about *how* a person is—about her mental or physical condition—unless *we* associate with 'old' characteristics such as awkward, incompetent, confused, inexpert, in need of help, absent-minded etc. If the word 'old' implies these kind of images, it is indeed derogatory, and understandable that so many people anxiously try to avoid it. Often, old people have, themselves, internalised such negative images and therefore deny, at any price, being 'old'.

Though these derogatory perceptions are hardly ever specifically or openly defended, they are there, subliminally, in the minds of many people and influence their way of dealing with old people. Lately, I have had a frequent taste of it, making me realise, 'I am old now'—even before actually feeling it. I have suddenly noticed certain people talking to me in different way. Not those close to me or those with whom I deal professionally but, in short, superficial contacts in the street, at the bank or at the supermarket. I have been confronted more and more with a new, unfamiliar note: patronising, didactic, benevolent but condescending, as if I would not know, for example, how to post a letter or how to behave at the bank counter or the supermarket till.

One of many examples: I want to withdraw money from my account and don't have my bankcard. I tell the young woman at the counter, showing her my passport instead. She serves me unwillingly, saying, 'Next time you must bring your card with you!' Or I drop something at the till of the supermarket and a woman of about forty picks it up saying, 'Don't drop your belongings, good woman.' I reply, 'Thank you, good woman' and, startled, she apologises. Or, the most blatant experience so far: At a countryside restaurant where I have lunch with a friend (who is a few years older than me), the waitress enquires, 'Normally we serve our local wine cooled. Is that OK for you, ladies—I mean because of the bladder, etc.'

Increasingly frequent experiences of this kind have made it clear to me that, at least in superficial encounters, other people perceive me in a way—old lady, a little awkward and not to be trusted with too much anymore—that doesn't quite fit with how I see myself. Each little mistake (and I am not fooling myself, these do happen more and more) confirms this image and seems to justify the admonitions. However, when my son forgets *his* bankcard, nobody speaks sharply to *him*, and when my daughter drops something, nobody calls *her* 'good woman'. Why?

That I don't just swallow such remarks obviously does not correspond to the image. My responding to prejudices that people themselves are often not even conscious of puts them off their stroke and provokes various reactions: irritation, embarrassment, offence and sometimes shame.

Unfortunately (and I hate to say it) it is predominantly young women who address me in this way, whereas it seldom happens with young men. On the other hand, there is rarely a man available to help me carry my suitcase up or down the stairs when the elevator at the railway station is, yet again, out of service. If anybody at all offers help, it is usually a woman. However, I have learned that it is also up to me to ask when I need help—and so far it has never been refused.

I don't mind when people realise my age and show consideration. In some situations I am glad to be helped. But having difficulty carrying a suitcase upstairs does not imply that I am slow on the uptake. Not that

I deny the changes that age brings. They are obvious and I notice them clearly: physical strength diminishes, certain things are more trouble and take more time than they used to, reactions become slower, hearing and seeing weaker, mistakes and forgetfulness increase. All this is restricting, time-consuming and sometimes annoying, but it is not a crucial influence on my awareness of life. These are tiresome but peripheral phenomena I have to live with. Sometimes they become unpleasant and embarrassing, but they don't define my identity. Self-awareness is not shaped just by the present but by our whole lives, whereas the external image reflects the here and now. When I look in the mirror I see my grandmother before I realise, still a little surprised: 'That's me!' The image in the mirror corresponds only partly with my body feeling in which the transformations of a lifetime are melding into a whole that embraces more than the actual external image. There is a discrepancy between self-perception and how others perceive us. Even though, with time, this discrepancy diminishes and the external picture gets slowly integrated into identity—a difference remains.

Anna O describes her experience: 'Sometimes, I try to look at me from the outside, I see the behaviour and reactions of an old woman and I think, "Oh, that's how it is now."' And Peter Q, way over eighty, still very active and mentally alert, ironically and self-critically expresses what he feels: 'It's only others who get old.'

However, life awareness does change; in one respect there is much more freedom—internally as well as externally. Nora L calls it 'Freedom to do as one pleases' and adds, 'When I was younger I felt the external pressure much more.' As for me, I deeply enjoy the freedom of no longer being constrained by so many obligations and considerations. And I feel freer now to be just as I am. This is one crucial aspect of my awareness of life which at the same time is shaped by

- evidence of limited time remaining,
- the certainty of approaching death,
- a pronounced need to concentrate on the essential.

These issues are much more present in my daily life than the small aches and pains that are also there. This does not prevent a faint fear of becoming demented and dependent on care lurking in the background—sometimes more sometimes less perceptible.

That 'the borrowed time is visible now on the horizon'—as the Austrian poet Ingeborg Bachmann puts it in a poem (Bachmann, 1953: 18)—is a strong drive reinforced by the sensation that time is running faster and faster, and the worry that there might not be enough left. I get impatient when projects progress hesitantly, decisions are put off and ideas can only be realised on a long-term basis. I know—I can't postpone what I want to achieve, it has to be done now. This is sometimes difficult to understand for people who still have time—I too used to believe that what can't be done now can always be done later. In the meantime 'later' has become an uncertain factor. On the other hand, I know that we never can realise everything in life, that something will always remain unfinished. This gives me a composure which compensates for the impatience. Both feelings complete and more or less balance each other.

Not only is time running faster and faster, it also seems to shrink in my memory. When I think something happened last year, it is usually already two years since. And when I feel 'that was ten years ago', it was actually twenty or even thirty years.

The certainty of death inexorably coming closer feels strange and ambiguous. That we must die some day is the only thing in life we know for certain and without any doubt. Yet, the nearer it comes the more unreal it seems. At least that's how I feel. Rationally, I know it, but emotionally, I can't really grasp it. I know that not too far from now I shall no longer exist and sometimes feel a little sad about it, but I cannot really figure it out. Perhaps it has to do with the fact that dying, for each person, is something entirely new, unknown, unimaginable, an absolutely unique experience that we have never had before and will never have again. We cannot refer to anything we know and nobody can tell us how it will be for us. The last stretch of road is one we have to travel alone, even when others, to some extent, try to accompany us.

The urge of limited time and the certainty of death approaching combine with the strong need to concentrate on what is essential. I tend more and more to concentrate on what is important and enjoyable for me and avoid having to struggle with irrelevant matters. Yet what *is* essential and what is irrelevant in these years of life? There is no general answer to that but a great variety of very different, individual replies.

For me, for example, it is important to be with people with whom a real exchange is possible. It is quite natural that, with age, there are less very close and familiar people. There are not many left to whom I can say: 'Remember?' However, new and pleasant encounters do happen— perhaps not so often, as with age we discriminate more and are less interested in superficial contacts; it becomes more precious to meet each other on a personal level. This does not imply that there must always be a sophisticated conversation; a good exchange might also develop about everyday matters if they mean something to the people concerned. A few words with somebody in passing can be delightful when the person behind the stranger becomes perceptible.

Work is still essential for me, but latterly my main focus has shifted more and more from therapeutic and consulting activities to writing. It has become, and hopefully will remain for some more years, an essential part of my life. I highly appreciate the freedom it offers me to mostly organise my time myself, which helps me to remain active. However, I also enjoy the other commitments that come about through my books—seminars, workshops, lectures—and would not yet want to do without them, despite their fixed (and sometimes tiring) time structure. It is deeply satisfying to see that what I think and stand for is being taken up and implemented. It encourages me and inspires further thinking and new ideas. And it feels good to realise that stressful days are still manageable, though it is true that they are more tiring then they used to be and that I need more time to recover. I have to make sure that there are not too many such days. Finding the right balance and being able to say no is crucial—and sometimes difficult. However, I would not like to have no commitments at all and to just revolve around myself.

Much more than work itself, it is all the things that go with it that I find tiresome: travelling, unpleasant accommodation, dreadful breakfast and dinner buffets in some places. So I try to organise the circumstances of these commitments to be as comfortable as possible. This is not a luxury, but a necessity if I want to spare my energy for my work instead of exhausting it with tiresome and trivial details.

Looking for the essential and dislike of the irrelevant not only relates to the major issues of life but also to the mundane daily details. I hate it when I have to wait, and have little patience with the trivial concerns of everyday life. Shopping, cooking, tidying up, taking my clothes to the dry cleaners, paying bills, calling the workmen because something in the house needs to be fixed—not that I dislike to do all this, but I find it increasingly tiresome because it takes so much time and prevents me from doing what I really want to do.

I find objects that I don't really need increasingly burdensome. I don't feel comfortable in a room crammed with ornaments, though when travelling this is sometimes unavoidable. At home, too, it bothers me when stuff keeps accumulating even though I constantly dispose of unnecessary things: I want the rooms to be as empty as possible, containing only what I really need, but despite my good intentions I never manage to achieve this.

I am well aware that lacking patience for routine tasks can result in people neglecting themselves and what is around them and I can empathise with those old people who do this. The daily jobs, once straightforward (clearing up, brushing teeth, laying the table, shampooing hair etc.), take more and more time and ask for a discipline too demanding when other things seem so much more important. Our changing perception of time plays its part here too. Although I thought that I took my vitamins this morning, it was actually yesterday; I changed the towels last week, but it seems a couple of days ago to me, and the vegetables I believed I bought yesterday have actually been in the fridge for five days. So I am on my guard. I have learned to mistrust my memory and always try to double-check. And, mostly, I resist the temptation to put the cheese on the breakfast table in its wrapping, to not clear the table and go straight to my desk in pyjamas so that I can get on with what I really want to do.

Good quality, in every respect, is much more important for me now than it used to be. I am choosier—be it about food, culture or relationships. Anna H feels the same: 'I am more demanding, internally as well as externally, above all with myself. I live with more awareness now.'

Quality, for me, does not mean that anything has to be exclusive or highly sophisticated. I love bread and cheese, but it has to be good. I like to watch a TV mystery if it's well made. But I don't want to listen to a mediocre concert and detest any form of dilettantism, as well meant as it might be. I prefer spending an evening by myself than in the company of people I have little in common with. I prefer drinking no wine to bad wine and I refuse to stuff myself with food I don't like. I feel that my whole being has become choosier and now asks only for what is doing it good—as if there is, here too, an awareness of limited time. Of course, a preference for quality conflicts with not wanting to spend too much time on everyday concerns. If I want a good meal I must spend more time on shopping and preparation. Again, it is a question of finding the right balance, but if ever I did feel like getting help it would be with these trivial concerns of everyday life.

I am aware that there is a danger, in restricting myself too much, of narrowing my horizons. Confining myself to the familiar—no longer taking risks or trying out something new; refusing to meet new people— would result in stagnation and isolation. I don't want to narrow my horizons in this way. So I am still ready to get involved with the new and unknown—which sometimes brings about unexpected discoveries. The computer, for example, that I have to use for professional reasons (reluctantly at first) has opened up a new world for me, in spite of only selectively using and understanding it.

I don't want to isolate myself but to participate in the world in which my grandchildren are growing up, to be concerned with and able to understand it. However, I don't feel obliged to understand or participate in everything. It seems to be part of the process of growing old to no longer understand everything in this fast-changing world—how else could we gradually prepare to leave it some day? Though I feel no need to appreciate everything that is new or 'in', I am far from glorifying the past or from joining in the chorus of 'everything used to be better in the past'. Not understanding something or not wanting to deal with it, in no way implies that it is bad. I can even sympathise with the irritation sometimes felt by younger people towards old people who always think they know better and consider their own values and norms to be valid for everybody. In addition, with demographic changes, the younger generation must sometimes feel like a minority. Even to me, though I am old myself, it feels odd sometimes to be (say in a train, at a concert, in a restaurant) almost exclusively amongst old people, and I too would prefer a better mix of generations. However, my generation is neither responsible nor to blame for being such a large group.

There are many things that I find much better today than in the past. However, if I don't like something, I don't feel obliged to carry it through just because I have started it. If at the theatre I don't like the performance, I leave at the break, even if it is promoted as the 'play of the year'. I don't have to finish a book which I find boring. To know that I will anyway never achieve everything I would like to, that there will always remain something unread, unseen, undone, gives me the freedom to choose how I want to spend my increasingly precious time.

I am aware that my body is demanding, more and more, its rights. When I was younger, it never occurred to me to take a nap during the day. Now I do that from time to time. When I get tired, I give in if possible (even at an 'inopportune' time) and sleep for a few minutes or, once in a while, even for an hour or two. I feel it important to listen to the rhythm of the body. I don't mind sometimes waking up at night for a while; I will read and catch up on my sleep in the early morning. It does not happen frequently. Nevertheless, I try not to schedule appointments in the mornings but use those to work at my desk where I am free to start whenever I am ready. Following the rhythm of our body means taking care of our personal resources.

Hours of leisure are as important as being active. To do nothing, enjoy the moment, think, listen to music, read (I can't imagine a life without reading), sit in the backyard, watch the clouds, be in my inner world—all this is part of life and takes its time, even though things that should be done must then wait for tomorrow.

These personal preferences and dislikes have an influence on my considerations about the future and what will happen, if some day I might no longer be able to manage things myself and need help. The prospect is not tempting and of course I am concerned, as I know only too well what I want—and what I definitely don't. I want to maintain what is essential for me and get support with *that.* I want to get the kind of help *I* need, not the sort that others, based on their ideas or on theories *they* have acquired, consider to be good for me. I want to be respected as a person, taken seriously and not reduced to my insufficiencies and deficiencies. I don't want to be patronised or educated. I don't want to be 'activated' or animated to do things I am not interested in. I want (within the limits of what is still possible) to be engaged in what is important for me. I don't want to be entertained with 'senior programmes' or to participate in special exercises 'for the elderly', but as far as possible to continue to do some yoga exercises, which I know do me good. I don't want to have to sing Christmas carols or to do handicraft work. And I want to be allowed to withdraw into my inner world whenever I feel like it.

I don't want, being urged by persons I hardly know, to talk about the events in my life *they* consider important when reading my files. Yet I want those memories which emerge *in my mind* not to be dismissed as fantasies because they seem unlikely to the carers. I want reactions coming from the background of my experience to be taken seriously, though they might be hard to understand for people whose experience is different.

I want to decide for myself if I get up or stay in bed a little longer, which clothes I want to wear, when I feel like listening to music or watching television, when to take a bath, wash my hair or cut my nails— even though I might need help with these things. I don't want to have to eat food I don't like or when I am not hungry. All this probably makes me not very suitable for life in an old people's home where I might be considered a 'difficult' and not very welcome resident. Other people have other preferences and dislikes and it is crucial for their well-being that these are taken into account. Olga S, for example, has made a written record of her wishes, in case she has to move to a nursing home. Among other things, she wants 'to be left alone when I am no longer able to occupy myself with something. Under no circumstances do I want carers to read me stories. If they absolutely must do something, I would prefer them to show me an art book'.

Why do I begin this book about care for old people with such personal thoughts? Not to suggest: 'that's how old people *are'*, but to give *one example* of how being old can be experienced. I would like to arouse sensitivity for the *many different ways to experience* being old. In addition, in these personal considerations, there are some keywords pointing to general issues. The limited time, death coming closer—these are existential conditions everybody is confronted with, but that are perceived and experienced differently by each person. Some people very consciously deal with these issues; for others they are, only vaguely, somewhere in the background. Some people deny or suppress them, others cover them with being busy all the time—there are many different ways of facing, or not facing, these aspects of life.

I know I am privileged to have work that I like and consider meaningful. It allows me to experience these late years as a full and delightful chapter of life. For many other people it is quite different. However, I am not an exception. More and more people feel these years to be a particularly good time. 'The time after retirement is the best chapter in life. What a pity that it is, at the same time, the last,' wrote Hans Meier in a newspaper opinion poll about how people experience old age. (*Neue Zürcher Zeitung*, 2004) However, there are also those for whom age predominantly means loss, restriction, decline and illness. Between these two poles lies a broad spectrum where any shade is possible.

This spectrum of various shades, nuances and contrasts, determines more and more the task of carers, therefore, sensitivity to the variety of individual experience is a basic requirement for sensible care or service. In every life there are essential as well as trivial things; what is trivial and what is essential depends on a person's individual experience and cannot be decided by others. Any kind of care or social service has to respect this. The aim should be to enable old people to spend their remaining time with what is essential *for them* and to relieve them of what is tiresome or of minor importance *to them*. Carers can do this only when they orientate on and take into account the subjective, individual experience of the person they care for.

The principles and methods of the person-centred approach meet these requirements fully and therefore are particularly suitable for this field. What are the characteristics of the person-centred approach and what does it mean, concretely, to work 'person-centred' in care for old people?

2
Foundations of person-centred work

The person-centred approach goes back to the American psychologist, Carl Rogers (1902–1987). Rogers developed a specific form of psychotherapy called 'Client-Centred Psychotherapy', now known as 'Person-Centred Psychotherapy'. His second book, *Counseling and Psychotherapy* (1942), received considerable attention; his third, *Client-Centered Therapy* (1951), made him famous worldwide. Later on, he expanded his concepts beyond psychotherapy and applied them in other areas (for example, groups, schools, organisations, institutions) calling them the *Person-Centered Approach*. (Rogers, 1969, 1970, 1977, 1980, 1982). In areas other than psychotherapy, the Person-Centred Approach has a different focus and develops different forms according to each specific field, yet the basic foundations remain the same. What are these foundations?

A humanistic view

A humanistic view considers each human being as a unique and estimable person and respects the differences between different people. Two people are never alike, not even when suffering from the same disease, showing the same signs of age or being in the same stage of dementia. The range of individual differences corresponds to a wide variety of ways of dealing with impairments and coping with daily life. A humanistic view assumes that each person, fundamentally, is aiming to grow, to develop her or his personal resources and to come to terms with reality. However, this aim can be impaired or disturbed for various reasons: developmental disorders, traumatic experiences, lack of support, diseases, impairments of old age, disorientation etc. But even then: *It is not we who know what is good for others, they know it themselves*, though their access to this knowledge might be buried. Helping people to regain access to their hidden resources and taking good care that the available resources don't wither away are significant tasks of care. The person-centred attitude is a crucial factor in carrying them out.

The person-centred attitude

Three elements characterise the person-centred attitude (Rogers, 1959, 1961):

Empathy (or empathic understanding) means accurately and sensitively grasping the feelings and experiencing of other people and entering their internal and external frame of reference as if we were in their shoes, but at the same time never disregarding the reality of being oneself and not the other person. Empathy does not mean identification. Empathic understanding does not aim at interpreting or categorizing others but at putting oneself as accurately as possible in *their shoes,* in *how they feel and experience.*

Acceptance (or unconditional positive regard) means, without judging, accepting a person as she is at the moment, including her problems and her potentials. It does not imply approving of everything a person does, but accepting that, for some reason, she has come to behave in that way. Not judging does not mean having no values but, on the contrary, being very aware of one's own values without imposing them on others. The values of old people are sometimes quite different from those of their younger carers. This must be taken into consideration and respected.

Congruence means that we are consciously aware of what we experience and feel and that we can discern it from what we perceive in the other person. Congruence means meeting the client as a person, not hiding behind a professional mask. It requires being aware of, admitting and accepting one's own feelings, impulses and impressions, yet not unrestrictedly throwing them in the other person's face. Carers must be capable of estimating when, and when not, in the context of their task, it is appropriate to express their feelings. Congruence further implies that the general conditions of the actual situation are clear and transparent for everybody involved.

A deeper understanding of what congruence and incongruence mean is provided by Rogers' theory of the self-concept.

The self-concept

The term *self-concept* (Rogers, 1951), though it is an important element of the person-centred view, has fallen somewhat into oblivion. This is regrettable because it can be extremely helpful in better understanding other people—particularly people whose behaviour is hard to comprehend. Self-concept is the image we have of ourselves and the value we attach to it. It develops from the child's immediate experience (for example, hunger, crying, being fed, satisfaction) as well as from the values communicated by the environment (for example: 'getting dirty is bad'). The self-concept is not a solid structure shaped once and forever but is constantly developing with the experiences people have in the course of their lives.

Disorders and emotional problems occur when experiences, feelings and sensations cannot be allowed because they do not correspond with a self-concept controlled by rigid values and taboos (for example: 'being angry is bad'), or because experiences, too painful and unbearable, had to be oppressed or reinterpreted in order to be able to survive (an extreme but unfortunately frequent example: sexual abuse.)

The individual assessment of experiences has a decisive part in developing the self-concept. At the beginning of life, it is an 'organismic valuing process' (Rogers, 1959, 1964). For example: babies cry when they are hungry or, their skin contracts when they are cold. Growing up, this valuing process changes in that the values the child is picking up from the people around them become more and more important. Adopting values from the world around is a natural part of the human growth process. However, these values must repeatedly be checked against experience and, if they don't correspond, be modified. Problems arise when internalised values are too rigid or too much in opposition to our well-being to withstand the comparison with our experience. This can result in being no longer able to acknowledge any experience that contradicts these values.

Incongruence means that *self-concept and experience do not correspond.* The self-concept is rigid and can accept only those experiences and feelings that fit into fixed narrow limits, whereas all others must be repulsed, oppressed, rationalised, denied, reinterpreted, or perhaps can no longer even be perceived.

Congruence means *correspondence between self-concept and experience.*
The self-concept is flexible and able to be aware of and to integrate new
experiences. Mental health is connected with congruence. A healthy
growth process implies that a person has developed congruence, is open
to her feelings and experiences and able to consistently integrate them
into the self-concept. There is a fluid border, though; nobody is a hundred
per cent congruent and nobody is a hundred per cent incongruent, but
the more pronounced the incongruence the more impaired is a person's
growth process and the more serious her psychological problems.

With the years, the flexibility of the self-concept decreases and slows
down. In old age we need more time to integrate new (and sometimes
not quite welcome) experiences into our self-concept. Some people (and
this too is individual) have a hard time giving up cherished ideas about
themselves and adapting their image of themselves to the changes which
age brings about. It needs time and might only proceed in very small
steps. If carers keep that in mind, they will find it easier to be patient and
not immediately qualify it as 'obstinacies of old age' or as 'losing sense
of reality' when somebody is sticking to ideas of himself which are no
longer quite realistic.

On the other hand, there are old people who identify themselves
with the negative qualifications they receive from others. Their self-
concepts then mainly consist in sentences like: 'I am not capable of
anything', 'I am of no use anymore', 'I am worth nothing'. It is essential
for carers to pay attention to not involuntarily reinforcing such negative
self-concepts but, on the contrary, emphasizing the resources that are
somehow still there in any human being, though perhaps hidden and
hardly perceptible.

The contact functions

Garry Prouty, the founder of *Pre-Therapy* (Prouty, 1994; Prouty, Van
Werde, Pörtner, 1998, 2002), with the term 'contact functions', defines
three levels of psychological contact: contact with reality, contact with
oneself (emotional contact) and contact with others (communicative
contact). In people with mental disabilities or psychiatric 'diseases', as
well as with old people who are disorientated or suffer from dementia, as
a rule, the contact functions are impaired. This might be so on all three or
on just one contact level, or on each level to a different degree, more or
less pronounced, constantly or only temporarily (such as in an acute
psychotic episode).

Pre-Therapy aims to develop and strengthen contact functions. Moreover, it can serve as a bridge to reach the isolated and hardly accessible, inner worlds of other people. The *contact reflections* Prouty has developed (Prouty, 1994: Prouty, Van Werde & Pörtner, 2002; Pörtner, 1996, 2000, 2007: 83–6) are a helpful method of establishing contact on all three levels (with reality, with oneself, with others) and—this is particularly important with old people—of stimulating contact functions and keeping them alive so that they will not wither away. Contact reflections are not a technique to be mechanically applied. Prouty emphasises that, again, the person-centred attitude is crucial. Based on this attitude, contact reflections can be extremely helpful in caring for old people. The following section will give a brief summary of the different contact reflections. (For more detailed descriptions *see above* and Van Werde & Morton, 1999.)

To the different contact levels, correspond different forms of contact reflections:

1. *Situational reflections.* The actual situation is reflected by very simple references to what is going on at the moment: 'We sit at the table', 'The lights are on', 'It is hot today', 'We are both silent', 'This room is big', 'You are playing with a pencil'. Situational reflections foster *contact with reality* in terms of the here and now.

2. *Body reflections.* Reflecting the movements or posture of the body stimulates contact with one's body, such as: 'You are very stiff', 'Your head is lying on your arms', 'Your foot jiggles up and down', etc. With people who do not respond to verbal communication it may be helpful to do the same body movement. However, this has to be done very gently, never as mimicry. The purpose is, by duplicating their body movements, to grasp more readily how the other person might feel at that moment and to meet them at the contact level on which they are actually functioning. Body reflections foster *contact with oneself* on the body level.

3. *Facial reflections.* Reflecting facial expressions, for example: 'There are tears in your eyes', 'You look happy today', 'You are frowning', 'You smile', brings people into contact with their feelings and also communicates to them how others are able to perceive and take an interest in their feelings. Facial reflections foster *contact with oneself* on the emotional level.

4. *Word-for-word reflections.* Reflecting word for word particularly makes sense with people who have difficulty in expressing

themselves verbally; who perhaps utter just faint, incoherent or unintelligible word fragments and sounds. If some isolated words or parts of a sentence are understandable we can repeat these, or we can repeat words or sounds that are not understandable but definitely contain emotions. With people who are able to formulate words, but handicapped in their articulation, in order to avoid misunderstandings, we should always repeat what we have understood, to give them an opportunity to correct us if necessary. Word-for-word reflections foster *contact with others.*

5. *Reiterative (or re-contact) reflections.* Reflections which have achieved contact are picked up again in order to re-establish the contact and stimulate it anew. The purpose of reiterative reflections is to *anchor contact* and to *strengthen contact functions.*

To re-establish, foster and strengthen contact functions, or to at least prevent them from being further weakened by alienating, institutional conditions, or by asking too much or too little from a person, is a major task in caring for confused old people. This task is, so far and on the whole, not sufficiently taken care of. Prouty's pre-therapeutic approach can easily be applied in everyday care, which offers many opportunities for using contact reflections. They are particularly suitable for coping with the different aspects of reality described in Chapter 7.

Yet, contact functions can be supported by more than contact reflections. A major part is also played by the way general conditions are designed. Here, Dion Van Werde's work is exemplary (Pörtner, 2000, 2007; Prouty, Van Werde & Pörtner, 2002; Van Werde & Morton, 1999). Van Werde is a psychologist and psychotherapist at the psychiatric hospital, Sint-Camillus, in Gent, Belgium, where he has organised a ward in such a way that everything serves the purpose of establishing and reinforcing contact functions. All areas are included: nursing, ergotherapy, leisure programmes, the weekly ward meeting with nurses and patients, as well as interior decoration. The examples Van Werde describes, though from a ward for acute psychotic patients, provide plenty of ideas for transferring these principles to other institutions, particularly organisations for old people who are disoriented, confused or suffering from dementia.

What does it mean to work in a person-centred way?

Not every method called 'person-centred' is truly person-centred. An essential aspect is *how* people work with these approaches. In order to immediately eliminate a frequent misunderstanding: person-centred work does not mean looking at the person in isolation from her environment and, in particular, it does not mean seeing the person as the problem. There is a temptation to do this with people who are disabled, mentally ill, confused, cranky, or in some way or other 'difficult'. Too often, carers tend to locate any problem that arises exclusively within the person. This should not be. Every problem involves social, institutional and interpersonal aspects that must be considered and examined. The influence of these factors is different with different people and must be understood in the context of their individual, internal and external, frame of reference.

In dementia care, particularly in the UK, several methods and approaches have been developed on the basis of person-centred principles; some of them include pre-therapeutic elements. A good overview is to be found in Ian Morton's book *Person-Centred Approaches to Dementia Care* (1999). In German-speaking countries, too, there is an increasing spread of certain methods that in some way derive from the person-centred approach, in particular Naomi Feil's *Validation* (Feil, 1982, 1992, 1993). Validation, on the one hand, is a developmental theory of people of advanced age and, on the other, a method to better understand the sometimes difficult behaviour of old people. Feil's method corresponds with person-centred fundamentals insofar as it is based on empathy and acceptance, but at the same time it implies a number of 'techniques' which, in practice, carers are often enticed to use mechanically. In addition, Feil uses some theoretical constructs that oppose the person-centred approach.

The person-centred approach does not work with interpretation, nor does it work with theoretical explanations, but aims at entering the world of other people and comprehending it from *their* viewpoint. Working in a person-centred way means *understanding, not explaining.* This is a crucial difference. Understanding means grasping a person from her frame of reference and her individual way of experiencing, thinking and feeling. This is the basic precondition for working in a person-centred way, which means finding ways and solutions *with* the people concerned, not *for them.* Carers should always keep it in mind: the nature of good care is *not 'making' but enabling.*

Working in a person-centred way is *more an attitude than a method,* though there are some guidelines concerning the methods to be used. An attitude cannot limit itself to big words but must be realised in the practice of everyday work, and there are more and less suitable ways to do this. From person–centred fundamentals some concrete, practical principles and guidelines can be deduced that define a framework for working in a person-centred way and, at the same time, provide useful criteria for controlling the quality of care. Even when based on person-centred fundamentals, a method should never be used for its own sake. It should be applied when—and only when—it is fully appropriate for this person, at this time and in this situation.

This is not a book about another therapeutic, teaching or nursing method, but it describes which basic conditions are necessary for working with person-centred methods, how the *person-centred attitude* is to be realised in *everyday care* of old people and its *concrete* impact on the ways of working.

Working in a person-centred way means:

- not going from a concept of how people should be but from how they are and from their potential
- trying to understand other people in their particular nature and way of expressing themselves and supporting them in finding—within their limited possibilities—their own way to cope with reality
- finding ways and solutions *with* not for the other person
- not explaining but *understanding*
- not making but *enabling*

3

Seven principles concerning old people

Person-centred viewpoints lead to some practical principles that are crucial in human relations in general, but particularly so in the care of old people. To realise these principles is fundamental to the quality of care and, consequently, to the well-being of those people being cared for.

Clarity provides safety and trust

Clarity is extremely important for people whose sense of orientation or memory is diminishing and for those who are temporarily confused or suffer from psychological problems; it is important in communication, information, support for orientation and in the design of the client's environment. Institutional procedures and organisational conditions must be transparent and comprehensive for everybody involved; everything must be conceived to serve the people being cared for and not (as is unfortunately often the case) the carers. For carers, clarity means being clear and comprehensible to the client, in attitude as well as language.

Why is this so important? Clarity is a precondition for successful communication, especially with people who are sometimes confused, disoriented, forgetful, or in some other way impaired. Such people particularly depend on clarity to help them cope with reality. Carers often underestimate this. However, not quite understanding what the matter is, or what they have to be prepared for, can provoke in old people whose thinking and comprehension is reduced or slow, strong feelings of insecurity and unnecessary anxiety, which are then perceived as inadequate behaviour by carers and other people. Again and again, we see how vague and ambiguous messages can destabilise the state of mind and reinforce, or even provoke, various psychological disorders, including psychotic episodes.

Social organisations do not always give clarity the importance it deserves. There is a tendency in this field to be vague, to give unclear information and to use a sophisticated, abstract, technical jargon hardly understandable to clients. In addition, the organisational structures are often not transparent. And, though clarity in person-centred work is indispensable, it is sometimes neglected by followers of this approach in favour of a cloudy idealism. This has, in the past, caused many misunderstandings and inhibited a broader acceptance of the person-centred approach.

In institutions, most attention to clarity tends to be paid to the design of the environment. There are often posters displayed in the hall or the living room indicating the actual date and day of the week. Others announce, perhaps even with a picture, which carers are on duty. The daily menu is stuck on the wall with other information, and routes through the building (to the dining room, the living room, the lavatories) are marked with different colours. Such clear visual information is of great help to people whose sense of orientation is declining, who tend to confuse times and places, are forgetful, or sometimes just completely absorbed in their memories. They cannot easily take in oral information or they immediately forget it, particularly when it is ambiguous or confusing.

However, it is as important to be clear and simple with oral information as it is with visual supports. What is clear to us is not always clear to others; old people are usually a bit slower in grasping things: they need more time and perhaps more detail because they have difficulty in connecting one thing to another, or because their experiential background leads them to associate differently from the way taken for granted by the carers. Therefore, carers must always make sure that information is received in the way it is meant.

Example
A carer enters Ms. B's room and tells her: 'Your son has called. He will be coming to see you soon.' Before Ms. B is able to digest the good news, the carer is gone. Ms. B gets excited because she thinks 'soon' means 'this afternoon'. She waits in vain the whole afternoon and is finally so disappointed that she cries.

What did the carer mean by 'soon'? Next week? Tomorrow? Or when? And what about Ms. B's orientation in time? The carer should have considered this and formulated her information appropriately. She could have spared Ms. B a lot of irritation and herself some unnecessary trouble.

Of course, there is the time pressure—but it should not serve as an excuse for such failures. The trouble and confusion brought about by lack of clarity takes infinitely more time—not to mention the nervous strain it causes on both sides—than taking care to communicate information in a way that is clear for the other person and adequate to her powers of comprehension and then checking to make sure that message came through.

With Ms. B, the unclear message meant that for several days (the son didn't come before the weekend) she repeatedly called the carers asking: 'Has John come? Is he waiting for me downstairs?'

Of course, even the utmost clarity cannot prevent or remove states of confusion. However, unclear information and ambiguous messages considerably contribute to, reinforce and even cause such states. This should be avoided at all costs, not only for the sake of the old people but also to prevent making the carers' already extremely demanding task even more difficult.

Individual experience is the key to understanding

Each person's way of experiencing is different. What is irritating for one is funny for another; what throws some people into a state of panic, leaves others indifferent. One person finds intrusive what, for another, is helpful. Individual experience is subjective.

This subjective experience is an important aspect of the person, a helpful key to understanding her and detecting her resources. This is not always given sufficient attention in care. We are not used to being aware of another person's experiencing but tend to take our knowledge and our norms (and sometimes our own subjective experience!) as the one valuable model for everybody. We overlook the fact that, for another person who experiences differently, it might not be of any use.

Nurses tell a patient what she must do to feel better instead of showing an interest in how that patient experiences her disease and in how she is trying to cope with it, and then finding ways of helping her to utilise her personal resources. Instead of being empathetic towards a person's way of experiencing and attempting to work with them to find a solution, carers try to persuade the person that the situation is not the way they see it at all

Example
A nurse enters Mr. U's room.
Nurse: 'How are you, Mr. U?'
Mr. U: 'Not too well.'
Nurse: 'Oh—but you look good.'

Mr. U says nothing.

The nurse makes several suggestions to Mr. U: 'Have a cup of tea', 'Go for a walk' etc.

Mr. U says nothing.

This is an example of what happens time and again in institutions—not because the carers are not interested in the residents' well-being, but because they have never learned to respond to a person's experiencing and are used to having advice and solutions immediately at hand—which, as we know, is not of much help if the other person does not feel understood and accepted in what she or he experiences. Changes can only be developed from individual experience, not from external assumptions. Feeling understood in their *experiencing* helps human beings to develop new ways of behaving. This is why it is so important in care and nursing to have empathy with the way another person experiences.

Example

Mr. S, a man in his eighties, has recently been moved to a nursing home. He is very confused and quite rebellious. He is incontinent and no longer able to wash himself but he fiercely refuses to be washed by the nurse and turns away from her so that she cannot reach him. The nurse tries to persuade him to turn around but this only makes things worse. The more the nurse tries, the more violently Mr. S defends himself. The nurse becomes more and more impatient then suddenly realises that an impasse has been reached. She relaxes for a second, takes a deep breath and tries to imagine how Mr. S might be feeling. Then she says: 'You feel embarrassed, Mr. S, because I have to wash you, that's why you turn away from me.' He turns around and docilely allows the nurse to wash him.

This example shows how helpful it is in difficult situations to try to understand a person's behaviour and the way he or she experiences the situation. Not only does it mean that the other person feels understood and taken seriously, it also helps to make the carer's work much more interesting and satisfying, without exhausting (and mostly vain) attempts to stop unwanted behaviour, or to persuade people that things are not the way they experience them. Understanding human beings through their individual ways of experiencing is not only invaluable in small, everyday matters but, by helping to avoid or defuse conflict, provides a better quality of life.

It is not what is lacking that is important, but what is there

Old people are usually judged—and judge themselves—by what has become more difficult for them or what they can no longer do. That there is something else blossoming is hardly ever perceived by carers or even by the old person themselves.

Yet, sometimes, confused old people develop amazing emotional and intuitive qualities or make connections which, however seemingly bizarre, make absolute sense when really thought about—perhaps not rationally, but as a picture or an association reflecting a deeper truth. And sometimes, quite unexpectedly, a new warmth develops within a lifelong difficult relationship.

Example

Ms. M is visiting her mother in hospital. At first, the mother seems confused and doesn't recognise the daughter sitting beside her. The relationship between them has always been problematic. The daughter has never been able to do anything right in her mother's eyes and has been constantly criticised. The mother has even complained to relatives that her daughter is a failure. Now, though, she opens her eyes and seems to recognise her daughter, who spontaneously hugs her. The mother says: 'It's so good that we can hug again.' The next day she dies. Ms. M considers this a very important moment in her life, reconciling herself with her mother—despite nothing having been talked through or resolved.

Paying more attention to what is there than to what is lacking does not mean ignoring a person's limitations (which would impede carers in providing necessary support): it is our perspective on those limitations that is crucial. Reality can only be coped with by dealing with those capabilities that are present *now*, not with those that are lost.

The potential for coping with change and for overcoming disability lies in a person's resources not their deficiencies. Carers must look for those existing (but perhaps dormant or buried) resources which, to some degree, could balance deficiencies and compensate for lost capabilities.

The principle of working 'resource-oriented' not 'deficiency-oriented' is gaining increasing acceptance in care for old people. However, 'resource-oriented' work usually concentrates on resources that are *still* there. That's not enough. Carers must be vigilant for what is there *now*—perhaps very unspectacular and at first not obviously a resource. Human beings, on this part of their journey, might need resources that are quite different from those usually seen as necessary. Forgetfulness, for example, in general considered a deficiency, might become a resource at a time of life when we need to get rid of unnecessary burdens.

Being old doesn't only involve a loss of the capacity formerly taken for granted; it also provides a certain degree of liberation. When a person is no longer responsible for the functioning of their daily life, they no longer have an urgent need for the corresponding skills and may develop other potentials which, having been previously unessential, have been lying fallow. A person who is no longer able to travel might start upon a journey within herself and discover something new or see something familiar in a new light. When the immediate reality is no longer perceived so clearly, images and memories might be stirred which seem more important than the immediate present—and the memories that are important to a person, the life events that are meaningful to her *now*, cannot be decided by anyone else. It is essential to respond to what is there, not to delve for what is lacking, has been suppressed, forgotten or left behind. Not everybody wants to talk about their lives—some people prefer to be alone with their memories, whilst others are happy to finally have an opportunity to talk about certain things; perhaps to rid themselves of things that have bothered them for years, that they have never previously been able to discuss.

Growth is a lifelong process

Growth should not be seen as a line going up and down on a graph, but more as a spiral. The last chapter of life is not simply a period of decline, though indisputably many abilities do diminish. It is also part of a process of growth leading towards life's end. There are major transformations to come to terms with now, physically as well as mentally; meanings and values, valid throughout life, are changing. The self-concept has to deal with, and integrate, these experiences. This growth process is sometimes painful because the changes this last chapter brings about are not always easy to accept. Many people experience them as negative, particularly if they are judged so by those around them. To see these changes as steps of growth opens a new perspective, making them easier to reconcile.

For carers, it is the adoption of another viewpoint that opens new ways of understanding; it is not about expecting, or even wanting, to initiate particular steps of growth. It is not for carers to decide what a person should learn, achieve or work through at this late time of life. However, carers must *be aware of, recognise and support* even the tiny steps of growth a person takes. These are rarely visible in a measurable 'performance' but in a change of inner attitude. For many people in this last chapter of life, their personal, inner world becomes more important than the external, so changes that from the outside appear as movement backwards, might now be steps of growth.

Example
Each morning at breakfast, ninety-two-year-old Mr. L has, until now, listened to the news on the radio. Two days ago, he suddenly decides he no longer wants to do this and tells the carers not to switch it on. They can't understand. 'But why, Mr. L?', they ask, 'You've always wanted to know what's going on in the world. You really don't want us to switch the radio on?' Mr. L shakes his head. At the team meeting the carers express their concern that 'Mr. L has further deteriorated'.

This could be seen differently. Mr. L has taken another step on his journey and the news of the day is no longer important to him. Is that really to be considered so negative at his time of life? I think, on the contrary, Mr. L could be simply letting go of something he no longer regards as significant.

Self-responsibility is existential

Taking responsibility for our actions is an existential need and an essential aspect of life. Human beings need to take responsibility for themselves in order to feel like functioning, acting people rather than heteronymous objects (subject to external law, not autonomous). Therefore, everybody must be, according to their individual potential and ability, trusted with and granted some responsibility.

Of course, with people in need of care, these possibilities are limited. However, this does not justify taking away *all* responsibility. Areas can *always* be found where people, even those with very limited capabilities, *can* take responsibility and where it *must* be left to them. It is a fascinating challenge for carers to find out where this is possible. It might be something quite unspectacular: deciding whether they want the door open or closed, or being asked if it is OK to be taken to the lavatory. This might appear banal to carers, who sometimes have more than enough responsibility, but for people who have had to give up so many of their responsibilities, these small everyday issues are meaningful. To take responsibility for oneself means, to some extent, still being master of one's life and not dependent on others for everything. This reinforces self-esteem and improves the quality of life.

The fewer the opportunities left for a person to take responsibility, the more important it is *not to completely remove them,* thus increasing helplessness, dependency and low self-esteem.

Example

Ms. W who, after a stroke, is paralysed and no longer able to speak, lives in a nursing home. A friend who responds to her very sensitively is visiting and Ms. W obviously enjoys the visit. A carer comes to clear the coffee table and suddenly remembers that a children's choir is giving a concert for the residents. Taking the wheelchair, he says, 'Let's hurry, Ms. W, there's something going on in the hall.' He then drives the flabbergasted Ms. W out of the room, without noticing the equally flabbergasted visitor, and without asking if Ms. W is at all interested in the singing children or would perhaps prefer to stay in her room with her friend.

Unfortunately, such disrespect towards old people's self-responsibility is a common feature of the daily life of institutions. The carer certainly meant well, not wanting Ms. W to miss the event. But 'meaning well' does not justify ignoring the wishes and self-responsibility of others, particularly those needing care, whose freedom to decide is, in any case, quite limited. This treatment can only result in them becoming more and more dependent and finally not trusting themselves to make any decision or take any responsibility.

There is more to a person than the present appearance

Another truism—but it is particularly true for those with a long life behind them. Even though, because of their disabilities, there might be little that is currently perceptible, people cannot be reduced to their outward appearance. Their background and past must be taken into account— even if nothing, or barely anything, is known about it.

Example

Eighty-five-year-old Ms. F, a highly educated former professor at the university, a well-known scientist and author of many publications, now lives in a nursing home, dependent on a wheelchair. She needs help in every area of her daily life but, until recently, was still busy with her scientific books. She is becoming weaker and, though not really suffering from dementia, her intellectual abilities are diminishing. She hates being taken in her wheelchair to the house events. She is not at all interested in what they offer: story readings, handicrafts, entertainment etc. Repeatedly, she has told carers and volunteers that she doesn't want to be taken to these events. Nevertheless, again and again, a carer has come to her room, saying, 'Oh, Ms. F, here you are again, sitting all by yourself—I'll take you to join the others', and has grabbed the wheelchair and pushed it to the living room. Ms. F needs a while to understand what is going on. Her protesting is useless. When a volunteer tries to talk about it with the staff, their answer is: 'Well, this way she is out of her room for a while and not constantly ringing the bell. We too need a little quiet from time to time.'

Although it is quite understandable that the constant ringing gets on the nerves of the staff, this is not the way to solve the problem. Ms. F's repeated ringing and her aversion to the house programmes are two different issues to be looked at separately. It should have been easy to anticipate that Ms. F would not be interested in the offered activities; most of the staff knew about her background. Very often this is not the case. However, knowing about a person's former life is much less important than *respecting that* there has been much more to it than carers have any idea about. Of course, it may help to know the biography of a person, but it is not always possible and not really necessary. The essential thing is to treat old people with respect for their whole person, including unknown aspects, and not to reduce them to their actual condition. *Respect for the unknown* in the other person is inseparable from the person-centred attitude and indispensable for sensible care. This attitude will be noticed by the persons concerned and have an influence on how they feel.

There is not just one (my) reality

The reality does not exist. Reality has many different facets that we cannot perceive all at the same time. There is the external reality: facts, objects, rooms, streets, cities, landscapes, seasons, weather and so on. There are also various personal and general events like a birthday, an accident, a change of train schedules etc; and then there is the internal reality of our feelings, sensations, experiences, dreams and reactions. There is no dividing line between these two realities: they penetrate each other. The external reality influences our moods and feelings; the internal reality influences our perception of the external reality. They are interwoven. So not only is the internal reality of each person different, the external reality is perceived differently by each person. This is clearly shown when several people describe the same place or event: the descriptions are never completely identical and sometimes differ considerably. Our perception is selective, which means we choose to see, or to overlook, individually, different aspects of reality—and tend to consider what *we* perceive as *the* reality.

We have a hard time seeing and accepting other people's perception of reality, just like our own, as partial aspects of a reality that is impossible to perceive in its totality. This impedes our understanding, particularly with those who are confused, mentally ill or impaired and whose perception of reality appears strange and unacceptable—in short, 'crazy'. To take other people seriously means acknowledging that their reality is different from our own. However, it does *not* mean identifying with their perception. This would be the opposite of congruent.

Carers should not, for any reason, try to fool others into believing that they share their perception—whether because it's easy, to get the person to do something, or to outwit them. Unfortunately, it happens all too often and is sometimes even promoted as a method. Morton describes an alarming example of 'how a hospitalised man with dementia had his belief that he was in a top-class hotel constantly reinforced and was even persuaded to take tranquillising medication by being "told that it had been sent specially for him by the management" (Wallace, 1996)' (Morton, 1999: 174). Such behaviour not only disregards the other person but also contradicts the principles of congruence and of taking other people's reality seriously. We have to accept that each person perceives another section of reality that is related to their personality and biography. This is not about fooling others but about communicating with them that we accept their reality as *theirs* as much as we accept our reality as *ours*.

If, for Ms. M, her internal reality is sometimes more prominent than the external reality, it is not necessarily only a matter of decline and disorientation, it could be that she is also preparing for a step of growth. When Mr. K and Mr. S describe an incident quite differently, it is because of their different biographies, experiences and moods: it doesn't mean that if one of them is right, the other isn't.

'It's another way to see it' is a useful and freeing insight, which not only makes it easier to understand other people but also broadens our own horizons. With people suffering from dementia, in particular, it is indispensable to be open to different aspects of reality. Chapter 7 will deal in more detail with the variety of realities.

Seven principles concerning old people

- Clarity provides safety and trust
- Individual experience is the key to understanding
- It is not what is lacking that is important, but what is there
- Growth is a lifelong process
- Self-responsibility is existential
- There is more to a person than the present appearance
- There is not just one (my) reality

4
Essentials for everyday care

From the principles already described, we can deduce some concrete guidelines for everyday work. These rules are not rigid but offer a structure for carers to orient themselves whilst allowing the leeway necessary to adapt to the individual person and to the demands of the actual situation.

Take the other person seriously

This is the foundation upon which everything else is based. Each person must be taken seriously in their individual way of being and of expressing themselves, even though this may appear strange, incomprehensible, confused or unrealistic. We have to respect that an attempt is being made to express something, even if it's something we can't understand. It is not always possible to penetrate the veil of confusion and comprehend bizarre ways of behaving. Yet if we accept that there is a meaning for the other person, even if we can't grasp it—rather than just dismissing their behaviour as absurd and incoherent and using labels like 'confused', 'crazy' or 'senile'—our accepting attitude will be perceived and will open the way for a much better quality of relationship. Trying to empathise with the perceptions and feelings of others broadens our own horizons and perceptions. Even *trying* to understand them facilitates a better approach to others, helping to discover hidden potential and awaken dormant resources—or at least keep alive and active those already there. Sometimes a statement that appears confused and improbable is much more relevant than we realise.

Example
Ms. M, a woman of 82, lives in a nursing home. Through a Spanish-speaking employee she is reminded of a trip she made to Argentina when she was eighteen. She tells the nurse about the crossing on an ocean liner and about the uncle who invited her to his country estate.

To the nurse this is an unfamiliar world in which she can't quite believe. As Ms. M is sometimes confused, the nurse dismisses her account as fantasy. Only half listening, she says 'oh' and 'really'. Ms. M notices this and gets upset. As it happens, Ms. M's daughter is visiting and knows that this trip to Argentina was a major event in her mother's life. The nurse is astonished and has difficulty accepting something that does not fit the image she has formed of this confused old woman.

What Ms. M clearly remembered, despite being sometimes confused, was an absolutely real and meaningful event in her life. By listening to her carefully and taking her seriously, the nurse could have learned a lot about Ms. M's world and biography and gained a new perspective on their relationship.

Needs and wishes must also be taken seriously, regardless of whether or not they can be granted. Even if, for good reason, a wish cannot be granted, there is a crucial difference between *accepting and acknowledging that the wish has been expressed* and criticizing or just silently ignoring it. We often have difficulty in discriminating and tend to equate 'accepting' with 'granting' so that if it is not possible to grant the wish (even though we would like to) we immediately reject it. Could this be because we find it hard to accept our own limitations—in this case, the impossibility of granting a person their legitimate wish?

'Taking seriously' means (this should go without saying but is not always practised) never talking *about* people in their presence but talking *with them,* even though they might seem to be 'not there' or 'non-verbal'. As a rule, people who do not speak take in much more than we suspect and are sensitively aware of any undertones used when we talk about them. This is too easily forgotten. The bad practice of talking about non-verbal, confused or demented people who are in the same room—in the erroneous assumption that they don't understand anyway—is customary in many families as well as institutions. This has a disastrous effect on the person's self-concept, leading to destructive images such as 'I don't exist anymore', 'I am nobody'. This is how confusion and loss of a sense of reality are reinforced, even provoked, instead of counterbalanced. The idea that people in advanced states of dementia become 'just empty shells' is an arrogant and dangerous assumption, neither proved nor compatible with the principle of taking people seriously. We know nothing about their internal worlds, how they perceive the external world or what they feel. Therefore we must become very sensitive to the subtle hints they give us.

Listen with all senses

Without *listening* there cannot be satisfying care or service. It is the foundation on which the person-centred attitude can unfold. Only by listening can we do justice to others. Carers, above all, must listen: to people with disabilities who have difficulty expressing themselves; to old people, even though what they express may seem unrealistic or confused; to nuances, hints for change, impulses, needs or wishes, feelings and moods. Listening is the precondition to understanding how other people feel and what they need and for finding the best ways to respond. Carers are not in a position to act or to take steps before they have listened. To be precise: it means listening *with all senses*—paying attention to reactions, feelings and sensations that are not verbally expressed.

Listening with all senses also means watching—not in order to observe and then judge behaviour, but to *feel into* the situation of other people and to discover *hints for what they experience.* Is Ms. U tense or relaxed? Does Mr. K look anxious or sad, or rather happy? Is Ms. E looking for close contact or does she prefer to withdraw? How does Mr. F react to what I do? What does Ms. H seem to like? What does Mr. B evidently find embarrassing? Care must be oriented on such hints—they sometimes tell us more than words.

Example
Mr. V is sitting in his wheelchair in the front yard waiting for his daughter to visit. Suddenly he calls for the carer. 'I have to go to the front yard!' he says. The carer shakes her head, 'But you *are* in the front yard, Mr. V! Your daughter will be here soon.' Mr. V becomes increasingly excited, repeating urgently that he has to go to the front yard. The carer keeps reassuring him that he is already there but Mr. V insists and becomes more and more upset. Finally, the carer hits upon the solution. 'Why don't you just show me where you want to go, Mr. V?' He points to the front door. 'There, to the front yard!' The carer steers him into the house. Mr. V, relieved, points to the lavatory door. 'There, that's where I have to go.'

Mr. V's urging and his increasing excitement were much more significant than the literal meaning of what he said. The carer was wise to respond to these non-verbal signals. She did not insist on proving him wrong but, instead, offered him an alternative to words to show her what he really wanted.

It frequently happens that old people, even though not suffering from dementia, mix up their words. In a mild form, this belongs (just like forgetting words) to the concomitants of old age which many people have to deal with. However, unlike those suffering from dementia, the error is usually realised as soon as the wrong word is spoken.

Respond to the person's experiencing

Care that aims at providing quality of life and well-being for old people must take into account their subjective experience. Only if carers pay attention to how a person experiences a situation can they deal with it in a sensible way. This also applies to quite simple things in the daily routine. Does Mr. G appreciate it when the radio is turned on, or is he annoyed by the noise? How is it for Ms. T to be washed by a male carer? Does Ms. K like it when the carer strokes her hair or does she find it intrusive? Is Mr. M happy when his wheelchair is placed at the table with the other residents or would he prefer to sit by himself near the window and look out? Is it nice for Ms. N when the sun shines on her bed or is the bright light blinding her? Carers must be observant of such things and try to, wherever possible, extend what is experienced as pleasant and reduce what is experienced as unpleasant.

It is not always possible to modify circumstances in the most desirable way, but simply acknowledging how people experience rather than just ignoring it will have a beneficial and relieving effect.

Example
A volunteer comes to take Ms. C for a walk. She finds her at the door of the nursing home, crying. A conversation reveals that Ms. C gets scared when other residents are quarreling. When this happens she wants to run away and vanish. After this, the carers pay more attention to Ms. C when it becomes too loud on the ward. They have a few words with her or take her aside so Ms. C feels less at the mercy of her fear.

It is essential that old people are able to feel that carers acknowledge how they experience a situation, even if it cannot be changed. Much too often, carers stubbornly try to correct the objective facts rather than responding to the subjective experience.

Example

Ms. H and Ms. D are good friends and spend much of their time together. One day, Ms. D loses her door key. Ms. H gets terribly upset and feels guilty about what has happened to her friend. Although not there when it happened, she cannot calm down and constantly repeats, 'It's my fault. It's my fault.' The carer tries to talk her out of this, but in vain. Ms. H repeats it over and over again. Finally, the carer tries something else: 'You are sad because Ms. D lost her key, right Ms. H?' Ms. H nods and soon calms down.

Responding to other people's experiencing is much more interesting, satisfying and useful than discussing facts. Old people in nursing homes often say: 'I'm going home now' or 'I want to go home' and sometimes get the answer: 'You *are* at home, *here*.' They become upset, begin to cry or quarrel, and a weary to and fro goes on. It would make much more sense to try to grasp the feelings behind their statement; for example: 'You're homesick', or 'You often think about your home, don't you?', or 'You are not quite settled in here yet' in order to make the other person feel perceived and accepted in how she feels.

Responding to the experiencing, and particularly to the feelings, of others is often unfamiliar to us; we are more used to communicating on a factual level. And responding to feelings and experiencing does not simply require empathy, it needs to be taught. 'Psychological accompanying', as I call it (*see* p. 54), should be part of the formative training of carers; attentive awareness, in accompanying a person's experiencing, should be subtle not intrusive.

'Knock at the door'

To 'knock at the door' (in a literal as well as a transferred sense) is a precondition to granting the respect for human dignity claimed in the statute of nearly every institution. Knocking at the door before entering a room should go without saying for all staff members, at any level, in order to respect the privacy of the resident. However, it is not the custom everywhere.

Example

A friend is visiting Ms. L at the residential home. They are in the midst of a conversation when suddenly an employee enters the room bringing the clean laundry and, without saying a word, starts to arrange it in the cupboard. The old lady sitting with her back to the cupboard hasn't initially noticed this and turns around, startled to see the employee. At the very least, the staff member should have knocked and said: 'I'm bringing you the laundry, Ms. L', or, even better, 'Is it OK for me to arrange this laundry in your cupboard now?' Ms. L might not have visitors very often and so would perhaps prefer to be left alone with her friend for now.

This might appear banal, but small issues like this can contribute considerably to a climate of mutual respect in an institution; as beneficial for the carers as the residents. This is equally important for people who don't seem to take much in, who hardly react, and from whom there is no 'Come in' to expect. It may be that, in some way or another, they are aware of the respect (or lack of it) for their privacy. Carers must wait a moment after having knocked, not (as one of them admits is their practice) 'burst straight into the room' after knocking. There must be a moment to allow the person to notice the knock and to prepare for somebody coming in—and for carers to stop, put aside what is in their minds and be open to the person whose room they are about to enter.

The principle of 'knocking at the door' can also be understood in a transferred sense. When a person has to be fed, washed, or taken to the toilet, it is necessary first to 'knock', i.e. to ask if it is OK for her or him. For the person to feel that they are being taken seriously and not treated as an object, this consideration is essential and applies to any nursing or therapeutic activity. Human dignity begins with privacy—physical as well as mental. Relying on nursing care means having to tolerate intrusions upon one's privacy, and this is embarrassing enough. Therefore, it is absolutely essential to first 'knock at the door' with a question or a gentle gesture so that the person is prepared and may have the opportunity to sometimes say 'No' or 'Not now'. This will not happen often, but will be less disturbing for the routine than the (unfortunately frequent) power fights with 'difficult' people who are constantly in opposition (they would be much less so if given a choice). To be asked, with words or gestures, means to be allowed to take personal responsibility. For carers, these might seem to be matters of no importance, but for the self-esteem of the person concerned it means a lot to realise, 'I too have something to say about this. It is not just determined by the carers. I am taken seriously.'

Conversations, walks, games, handicrafts etc. should never be imposed on old people, but offered as something to which they can say 'Yes' or 'No'. Even with confused people who are not able to answer, or perhaps to even understand questions, it is still possible to detect non-verbal indicators as to whether they like something or not. Paying sensitive attention to these indicators is part of good care.

Foster a person's own ways

With good reason I do not talk about autonomy here but about a person's own way. It is commonly agreed that the autonomy of old people has to be supported. However, on closer inspection, it appears that 'supporting autonomy' often implies a clear concept about what they should do 'autonomously' (in other words, only *certain* tasks) and they are not always asked if this is what they want *themselves*.

Old people have a right to be helped with what is difficult for them and this right must be respected. They have a life behind them, they have achieved something; now they need both to lean back and be helped and to do things themselves; what they want, when, and to what extent, is individually different and up to them to decide. Some might appreciate help with getting dressed, while others might prefer to dress themselves, even though it takes more time. It is these different needs—not what is easier for the carers—that must be decisive in the kind of help a person is given, otherwise fostering autonomy may easily become patronising and a way of imposing what the carer wants.

For old people, doing things their own way can also mean occasionally staying in bed for the day or not participating in an excursion organised for the residents. Doing something in one's own way always means taking responsibility for oneself (and people need this in order to feel like active beings rather than objects) and old people must, wherever possible, be granted the opportunity to do things their own way, even though they might not behave as the carers would like.

Example
Ms. A, 96, lives in a nursing home. Her thinking has remained very clear and she is happy that she is still able to walk. Nevertheless, she sometimes expresses the wish to die soon, and she sometimes refuses to eat because she just does not feel like eating. The nurses regularly admonish her, 'If you don't eat, soon you will not be able to walk anymore.' They know how important it is for Ms. A to be able to walk, and hope, in this way, to motivate her to eat.

Nothing justifies this attempt at intimidation. On some days Ms. A has a good appetite and enjoys her meal, so there is no reason to patronise her and not to respect her autonomy. To constantly admonish her, saying, 'You should eat, Ms. A', is unnecessary and out of place.

To respect a person's own way includes taking into consideration her or his individual rhythm. In the latter years, it is no longer so easy to outwit the body; it demands its due and doesn't like being locked into strict schedules. To eat when one is hungry, to sleep when one is tired, is a source of energy that must be acknowledged. It is ridiculous and useless to stress the body unnecessarily, especially at a time when strength is waning anyway. Of course, in an institution, there must be some kind of a daily schedule. But to wake old people at fixed times instead of letting them sleep damages their health. And it is not an unreasonable extravagance to occasionally warm a meal in the microwave when somebody has slept through a mealtime. Moreover, it is very important for old people to have an opportunity to turn the light on at night and have something to drink or eat because 'the process of dementia is accelerated when the blood sugar level repeatedly gets too depleted at night,' (Grond, 1984/1992: 80). That still 'in some residences for aged persons there is a space of 14 to 15 hours between dinner and breakfast and the confusion caused by low blood sugar level is made worse by tranquillizers' (ibid.) is not only a bad habit but a neglect detrimental to the residents' health.

Pay attention to and encourage small steps

Their decreasing abilities make many old people feel insecure; they lose courage and sometimes don't even trust themselves to do things that they actually are capable of. Of course, these feelings should not be met with cheap encouragement such as, 'Well, it isn't that bad, is it?' However, carers have to carefully pay attention to and acknowledge and reinforce the tiny steps a person is still, once again, or suddenly, able to succeed in. Even tiny, unspectacular steps should not be submerged in daily routine but be perceived and encouraged.

Old people whose abllities are declining primarily see what they cannot do anymore. And the feeling of insufficiency, of staying behind, becomes so omnipresent and overwhelming that they are not aware of how they still succeed in partial steps, or create little substitutes that to some degree make up for lost skills. They are not really aware of the importance of these occasional successful small steps. However, even the tiniest step is important since it proves the ability to take steps and bears the potential for further steps. Carers, therefore, should look for these tiny steps with a magnifying glass. Each step gives cause for hope and courage and counterbalances resignation and dejection.

Example

Mr. L, who has recently moved to a residential home, is very awkward with eating. His hands tremble because of Parkinson's disease. Food is always falling from his spoon and fork, and around his place at the table there is a mess. The carers don't say much, knowing that it is caused by Mr. L's disease. Nevertheless, they are obviously annoyed. Of course, Mr. L can sense this; it makes the nervousness he already feels in these new surroundings worse and he spills even more. After some weeks, he has settled down a little and feels more quiet. Of course, his hands are still trembling but, as he is no longer so nervous, he spills considerably less. Unfortunately, the carers don't notice the difference but just see that there are still stains around his plate.

It is so important, though, to draw Mr. L's attention to the small step he has taken and to show him that it is acknowledged. This will encourage and make it easier for him to live with his disease and the impairments it brings.

Provide support to act independently

Instead of just realising that someone is no longer capable of doing something and doing it for her, it is much better to offer specific support that helps the person to reconcile this incapacity and, to some degree, act independently.

Sometimes in institutions, old people are served a meal which, even though they don't touch it, will later be taken away, possibly with the reproach: 'You didn't eat again, Mr. X.' The fact is ignored that, depending on their condition, some old people are still able to take single steps, but can't combine them anymore. They need a little support such as: 'Now you must take the spoon', 'and now open your mouth' etc. Time pressure is no excuse for examples like the following.

Example

The carer puts the plate in front of Ms. P saying: 'Enjoy your meal.' When he comes back later to clear the table, the meal is still untouched. Carer: 'But, Ms. P, don't you want to eat today?' Ms. P: 'I do want to but I can't.' The carer, without saying anything more, takes the food away.

It is the carer's duty to find out what support Ms. P needs to be able to eat. Diagnostic information might make the carer's task easier by providing hints about the nature of Ms. P's difficulty but, above all, together with Ms. P, he should find out *what exactly* she cannot do and *where exactly* she needs support. On no account can it simply be accepted that she does not eat, since she has clearly communicated that she would like to, but can't. But often the necessary attention and care is simply not there.

Example
A carer admonishes Ms. X who is sitting in her easy chair: 'You are not drinking enough, Ms. X. If you don't drink we'll need to put you on a drip.' The daughter, who is the room, has to draw the carer's attention to the fact that the cup has been placed on the night table—out of Ms. X's reach.

On the other hand, there are old people who just eat very little, as we have seen in the example of Ms. A. It is important that carers can discriminate between a person who has no appetite, and therefore doesn't eat, and one who is no longer able to manage the process, and therefore needs support. This awareness is often lacking in contact with people in need of care (not only in relation to meals) and unnecessarily increases the helplessness of old people who then will not get the support they need to act independently. Such humiliating neglect may be caused by ignorance about the process and possible effects of certain diseases, by stress, by time pressure or sometimes just by thoughtlessness. Here, institutions should act immediately to improve things by training the staff, setting other priorities in terms of organisation, and finding ways to avoid situations like those described above. (One imaginable solution would be mobilising volunteers to help with the meals.)

Offer choices

Having choices and the opportunity to make their own decisions has a crucial influence on people's quality of life. It makes a difference to the way old people feel to realise they still have a choice, can influence things and take responsibility for themselves—be it only in the small matters of daily life. There is a benefit in not just feeling ignored and organised by others, but in still having a say.

It makes a difference for Mr. L's well-being if he can take a bread roll himself from the breakfast basket or if it is just put on his plate; if he can choose the jam he likes or is given one by the carer. It makes a difference for Ms. S to be asked how much milk she would like in her coffee this morning and for Ms. V to be able to say when she would like her nails cut or her hair shampooed. Such apparently banal details have a considerable impact on the well-being of people whose scope for action is already quite limited.

Look for the concrete

Besides responding to feelings and moods, there is another area that should not be ignored: What concrete needs are hidden behind a specific desire or an obscure dissatisfaction? It is worth looking more closely for concrete aspects, particularly those that might lie behind insistent, unrealisable wishes and general complaints about things that cannot be changed. What exactly is it that this person is missing or irritated by? Sometimes, even though the general circumstances can't be changed, small details can be adjusted that will improve or facilitate something for that person.

What does Mr. H associate with his wish: 'I want to go home'? Obviously, it expresses some of his feelings about moving into an institution and about how his life has changed—his nostalgia, sadness, melancholy or anger—and it is important to understand and accept these feelings. But there may be something concrete that he is missing or that is weighing on him; something that could easily be changed to make life more pleasant for him.

Looking for the concrete means not just rejecting 'impossible' desires but taking them seriously and thinking over possible partial solutions. This, in itself, does the person some good and perhaps, behind these desires, concrete needs that can well be met will become visible—at least partially. If carers succeed in detecting the concrete core of wishes that at first seem to be absurd and unrealisable, many an unhappiness can be resolved, or at least alleviated.

Find the other person's 'language'

Finding the other person's language is indispensable in making contact with her or him. Carers must both *understand* the language of their clients and *use a language that is understandable to them.* Professionals don't always realise how strongly their language is shaped by jargon, adopted during training and in dealings with colleagues, which bears no resemblance to how the people they work for express themselves. Yet it is not just a matter of avoiding professional jargon but, crucially, of finding a language that is understandable to the other person and close to his or her experiencing. To find the other person's language (and 'language' here embraces not only verbal but any kind of expression) means illustrating, making visible, describing things in a way that is comprehensible for the other person. With some people it may be appropriate to use images, whilst others will need a logical explanation; and it is often as much about the 'right gestures' as the 'right words'. This is particularly important with people who suffer from dementia and are no longer able to express themselves in familiar ways. Here, pre-therapeutic contact reflections are extremely helpful.

Example
Ms. L, suffering from Alzheimer's disease, was recently moved to a nursing home. The nurses cannot reach her. She either lies apathetically in her bed or runs yelling through the ward, which is disturbing for the other residents as well as the staff. All attempts to calm her, to quietly sit down with her somewhere, are in vain. Finally, a nurse who has participated in Pre-Therapy training, tries body reflections, running besides Ms. L and yelling too. She does this for quite a while (slowly becoming exhausted) until Ms. L suddenly stops running, hugs the nurse and starts sobbing loudly.

Thus, the nurse learns that Ms. L is sad and she can respond to that; contact gradually develops between them and Ms. L becomes much calmer and less agitated.

It is a mistake to believe that people who don't speak are necessarily inaccessible by language. Very often their *receptivity* for language is much more developed than their capability for verbal expression.

Example
At the nursing home, it is the general opinion that Ms. Y, who does not speak and always appears totally absent, is not reachable by language. But the physiotherapist has observed that Ms. Y frowns when she tells her, 'I have to go now' and smiles at her promise, 'I will be back tomorrow.' She doesn't know exactly what Ms. Y is taking in. Is it the tone, the emotional quality, or does she somehow get the sense of the words? She doesn't always show a reaction to what the physiotherapist says but it is obvious that she sometimes grasps something.

This example shows how necessary it is to speak to people who don't speak themselves. There is a chance that *sometimes, something* might reach them which should not be missed.

Even when people are declining, no longer able to express themselves, and seem not to understand anything, we must talk to them with respect for their human dignity. The example of Ms. G, who has suffered from multiple sclerosis for years and lives in a nursing home, shows how painful and humiliating it is when carers talk to old or ill people as if they were little children.

Example
Ms. G's disease has reached an advanced stage. She is no longer able to either move or speak and has practically no means left to express herself. The nurses—most of them relatively new and knowing Ms. G only as she is now—talk to her in a reduced, simplistic baby language as if this were all she could understand. A visiting friend, though, sees in her eyes that Ms. G is subtly taking in what she is saying and that she is happy when an issue she has always been interested in is touched upon. Ms. G is an educated woman who formerly worked as an art critic. It is painful to hear the way the nurses talk to her and it shows in Ms. G's eyes that she feels humiliated.

Knowing the biographies of people no longer able to express themselves in ways that we are used to may help carers to find the right tone with them. However, much more essential than such knowledge is *listening with all senses,* as described earlier in this chapter. It is, and remains, the most important access to the inner world and 'language' of another person. Knowledge alone might make carers prejudiced.

Don't let your guide be what you already know

If the nurse already knows that Mr. F will be aggressive when she enters the room and that Ms. M regularly spits out her tea, and enters the room with this expectation, it will, in all probability, happen. Our expectations influence the behaviour of other people more than we would believe. The well-known phenomenon of the 'self-fulfilling prophecy', in care too, plays an ominous role. People with limited intellectual capabilities develop sensitive antennae for what is implied and intuitively react to people's prejudices.

Carers should never assume they can predict with certainty how a person will react, even when it has been demonstrated hundreds of times. At any time, it is possible that a person will suddenly behave in a completely different way. Therefore, reporting between carers is double-edged. On the one hand it is useful for the carer, when he starts work, to be prepared for the fact that Ms. R has been very irritable all morning, but there is the chance that Ms. R will behave quite differently with someone who is unaware of what has happened previously. Therefore it is a good thing for the carer to be aware of the information but then to immediately put it aside in order to meet Ms. R in as unprejudiced a way as possible.

The same is true with regard to existing knowledge about biographies and habits. It might be informative for carers, but only if they remain open to new, unknown aspects of that person and don't become fixated on what they know.

More important than knowing about biographic dates and facts is attentive awareness to what, in some way or other, verbally or non-verbally, this person is trying to express. The 'biographic methods', so popular nowadays and worked with in many organisations, are helpful and make sense only when carers, instead of using the biographic data *they* consider important, pay attention to what is brought up by the persons themselves. Carers may sometimes ask a question or take the initiative, but they must immediately drop it when it is not picked up by the other person. On no account should a person be pushed into dealing with a particular biographical event just because carers think it might be important. Even worse is when carers, based on theories they have learned or read about, try to interpret biographies. Only the persons themselves know what a particular event in their life means to them.

Knowing about people's former habits, preferences and aversions might be useful on condition that carers do not tie the person down to them. If carers do try something that they have been told has worked in the past, they must carefully check the person's reaction. It is not necessary to ignore all knowledge about a person—it might well be a door-opener. But carers should *never let themselves be dominated by this knowledge*.

The same thing applies to specialist knowledge. As important as it is to know some basic things about dementia and other diseases and changes in old age, it always has to be very clear that theories and diagnostic categories are a *framework for the observer,* intended to facilitate *understanding* of other people and problematic behaviour. Others are not entitled to say: 'That's how this person is'. The essential is to be found beyond the framework: the unique and particular nature of this person. Each human being is, in some way, an exception, because the same disease never has exactly the same effect on every individual, nor does each person experience it the same way. Predominately orientating on categories blurs the view to what is beyond: the individual peculiarities and resources of a person. Kitwood noticed that at times some people behave in a much healthier and totally different way than would normally be expected at their stage of dementia. He developed concepts of care that take this into account (Kitwood, 1997a). To not perceive and to reinforce such 'islands' accelerates the process of dementia—thus causing an effect that is the complete opposite of what sensible care should actually be aiming at.

Our foreknowledge influences our actions and these have an impact on the people in our care. Therefore, the next and last guideline is probably the most important and offers the most opportunities to change something and to improve or defuse a difficult situation.

Recognise one's own part

This is necessary in two ways: on a personal level (which will be dealt with in the next chapter) and on a practical level, in daily life. In the context of these guidelines, it is about what can be done and about the simple fact that, at all times, every person involved contributes to how a situation develops. And changing something about one's own part is much easier than changing other people's behaviour. Therefore, it is crucial to clearly recognise one's own part—not in the sense of a reproach, such as 'I did it all wrong' or 'It's all my fault', but to try other ways of behaving. To change our own behaviour is usually the only way to change a dead-end situation and this is particularly true when a situation is escalating, going round and round in circles, or happening repeatedly in the same way.

The question, 'What can *I* do to change something?' is the first step towards overcoming helplessness and impotence and being in a position to act. There is *always something* we can change about our own behaviour. Again, it is useful to look for concrete clues to appease the situation and avoid escalation: How did the dispute begin? To what exactly did the other person react so irritably? What was I doing when she suddenly started to yell? And so on. Furthermore, external conditions often have an impact: Were we alone or were other people in the same room? Was the door open or closed? Was it noisy around us? etc. Very banal details could give carers a hint as to how they might change the situation *a little* and, with this, give the other person a chance to behave (perhaps just a little) differently too.

For a man who cannot move or speak and must be fed, there is a difference between the carer putting the spoon with the food between his closed lips and, alternatively, giving him a chance to open his mouth himself. This is just an example. There are numerous situations in daily life where carers, by changing their own behaviour, can give the other person a chance for change. What might be appropriate for some will not be so for others; it is worth trying different variations. Even if the person concerned is not always able to take advantage of the opportunity, a difference will have already been made by changing their behaviour, and the situation *for the carer themselves* will become more tolerable. This, in itself, will ease tension and prepare the way for further improvements, which everybody involved will benefit from.

Yet, in a much broader sense, recognising one's own part is a basic precondition for dealing appropriately with people who, in some way or other, are in need of care. More than we suspect (or would like to believe possible), our prejudices influence not only the behaviour but also the physical and psychological well-being of the other person. Carers, therefore, must be clearly aware of the images and ideas they have in their heads so that that these will not have a negative effect on other people—and, consequently, on themselves. In any profession connected with care, nursing or education, a qualification in the subject is not the only requisite for being 'professional': the right human qualities are just as important.

Essentials for everyday care

- Take the other person seriously
- Listen with all senses
- Respond to the person's experiencing
- 'Knock at the door'
- Foster a person's own ways
- Pay attention to and encourage small steps
- Offer support to act independently
- Offer choices
- Look for the concrete
- Find the other person's 'language'
- Don't let your guide be what you already know
- Recognise one's own part

5

Professional and personal competence

Although often played off against each other, professional *and* personal competence are necessary in the care of old people. Carers are challenged in many ways: people in their care represent a broad range in terms of individual needs, states of mind and health and this has led to a similarly broad range of professional and personal demands that make it indispensible for carers to acquire professional qualifications.

Professional competence

What does professional competence consist of in this field? Usually, carers have a basic training as nurses, sometimes as social workers, sometimes with additional knowledge in gerontology. There are also numerous people from other professions working in this field who, in parallel training programmes, acquire the necessary professional skills—or at least, should do so: the necessity of such training is not always sufficiently recognised. The belief exists that no specific professional skills are needed in the care of old people, that common sense and being human are sufficient—at least with those who don't need specific medical care. Such considerations do not always focus on the old people and their needs but are influenced primarily by finance, ideology or other agendas. Sometimes they just serve as a justification for lack of training or economy measures.

On the other hand, there is an (equally questionable) tendency to over-professionalise aspects of care. When a shopping expedition or any kind of outing with an old person is promoted as a 'project'; when every activity or occupation that might be good for a person or please her (exercise, knitting, singing or looking at pictures) is declared a therapy; when the experiences of human beings are reduced to (depending on the environment—medical, psychological or socio-educational) special terms, it is no wonder that many people mistrust, or even reject, 'professional competence'. In the same way, it is questionable that 'unfortunately professional competence is frequently confused with lack of concern and being self-opinionated' (Irblich, 1999). Though Irblich's statement refers to the care of people with mental disabilities, it also applies to the care of old people. On the other hand, the person themselves or their family sometimes have quite unrealistic expectations in relation to the omnipotence of professional competence: disabilities should be eliminated, signs of old age and decline 'repaired' by some kind of therapy. This might sound a little exaggerated but it is not far from reality. Yet all this is not what I understand by necessary professional competence.

So what is professional competence? Is common sense and being humane and natural incompatible with special knowledge? The opposite is true: *humaneness is an indispensable part of professional competence— and professional competence the precondition for being humane* when working with people in need of care. In any profession within this field, personal and professional qualities form an indivisible whole.

In the care of old people, professional competence not only consists of theoretical and methodical knowledge and the skills attached to specific tasks but, more importantly, requires of carers particular personal qualities. Special knowledge in different subjects is the necessary foundation for being able to handle the variety of tasks that care of old people requires. However, it needs more than that.

Personal aspects of professional competence

Congruence
As we have seen (p. 14), congruence is one of the basic conditions of the person-centred attitude. It asks carers to work on *themselves*, to recognise their own part in difficulties and conflicts, not only in terms of daily life but also on a very personal level.

Congruence is not a once and for all achievement but a constant struggle. Other people, especially when their behaviour is difficult or hard to understand, are always confronting us with ourselves, therefore the most important requirements for this work are:

Self-reflection
To meet other people without prejudice, carers must
- become clearly aware of their feelings, reactions, likes and dislikes, and be able to put them aside so that they will not inhibit their contact with other people.
- know their blind spots so that they are not dominated by them but open to the other person.

An open mind for the 'otherness' of other people

Being open to, interested in and tolerant towards the (perhaps sometimes strange and unintelligible) 'otherness' of the other person (a different background of values, experiences and existential conditions) is an essential requirement in this work. Without this, carers will not be happy with their job and will rapidly burn out.

It is not up to carers to transfer their own values and ideas onto the people they care for. On the contrary, it is the views and values of those they care for that carers must, as far as possible, be open to, respect and take into consideration. To understand, and take seriously, human beings in their particular individual nature is an essential aspect of professional competence, requiring that carers:

- use their knowledge and resources in a way that doesn't serve their own ambitions and preferences but the well-being of those in their care.
- accurately and subtly perceive the possibilities and limitations of other people and offer them the particular individual support they need.

These personal aspects of professional competence are as important as special knowledge in nursing or social psychology and to some degree learnable, and it is to be hoped that future training for care will seek to foster and evaluate these personal qualities; anybody working in this field should have the opportunity of and be committed to acquiring these crucial elements of professional competence in internal or external training.

Carers must take good care of themselves

This is indispensable to being professional and meeting the demands of these jobs. Unlike musicians, carers do not have an instrument to play and put aside—carers *are* the instrument and, like a violinist, they must tune, keep in good shape and take good care of *their* instrument—themselves. What does this imply?

Our private lives are of crucial importance in the fulfilment of personal needs: this is where compensation and recharging of batteries, both physical and mental, have their place. The necessary conditions differ with each individual, and how they shape their lives is a person's own responsibility. Of course, it is not always in our power to live in the way we would like. In every life there are ups and downs, times of crisis and periods when our needs and wishes cannot be sufficiently met. But, when working in this field, it is imperative—much more so than in other professions—that private problems and frustrations do not affect the quality of work. It is after all human beings, not products, that will suffer. This certainly does not imply that carers should always be happy or even pretend to be; again, this would be the opposite of congruence. Carers need not deny their feelings but must deal with them in a way that allows them to remain open to the people in their care whilst continuing to carry out their tasks; this too, to some extent, can be learned.

Another important factor in taking good care of themselves is *how* carers do their work. The esteem they show old people reflects back on the carer: lack of respect for the dignity of others violates the carer's own dignity. If their priority is not the well-being and contentment of their clients but their own ideas and ambitions, carers will hardly be happy with their job. Being interested in and benevolent towards what is different in other people is not only a necessary condition to adequately meet them but will also broaden and enrich the carer's own view of the world and human beings. Focusing, not on deficiencies but rather on what is there, and supporting and encouraging it, not only benefits the other person but the carers themselves; it saves them from monotonous routine and allows many surprising insights. Respecting other people's individual ways and, wherever possible, allowing them self-responsibility, improves both the clients' and the carers' quality of life, making their work much more pleasant and less exhausting.

Example
Liz has a new job in a nursing home. Initially, she works alternately in two different groups. She reports: 'With group A, I constantly make errors and am reprimanded by the head nurse: "Mr. X is not getting enough milk in his coffee, Ms. S is only getting half a cup" and so on—every detail of the day is meticulously regulated'. After a day of working with Group A, Liz feels stressed and nervous; in fact, the whole team is stressed and worn out. With group B it is totally different. Things are much looser, the clients are always asked how they would like things to be today—and it is absolutely not always the same. 'After having worked in Group B I feel relaxed in the evening and satisfied, thinking that it's been a good day,' says Liz. What is surprising is that Group B needs more care than Group A, so working there should actually be *more* intense.

This example emphasises the importance of choice and of giving responsibility to people in care and shows how this makes life easier for carers as well.

Recognising limits

This is necessary both for taking good care of oneself and for doing a good job. Nobody can always do everything right and solve all problems. There are sometimes situations where carers reach limits: their own, those of the other person and those of the given framework. And there are situations where it can be legitimate for a carer to ask: 'What can I do to make things more tolerable for myself?' It is crucial in such situations to be honest about reaching one's limit and not pretend to be acting in the client's best interests. If the carer feels better, it will in any case have a positive effect on others. Personal limits, of course, should not be so narrow that they will impede carers from fulfilling their tasks; in fact, carers must continually reflect on those limits to see if they can be expanded to some degree. It might be necessary and helpful to ask for consultation or supervision with this.

Being so challenged on a personal level can sometimes be a burden. A carer might feel himself to be sufficiently balanced; he might not feel inclined to constantly work on himself, preferring to let things stay as they are. It is not always agreeable to discover certain things about ourselves. Yet, on the other hand, isn't it a real chance to discover new aspects of our personality, to grow and maybe detect resources in ourselves we had never suspected before? There are not many professions offering this opportunity.

The limits of people in need of care have to be respected as well. Even if preconditions and requirements are met, there is no guarantee that everybody will feel good and be happy. The person's own part too is of importance and cannot be changed by the carers. What carers can do is to offer the best possible conditions, but it is up to the clients how they make use of these. Carers must realise this and not stress themselves by thinking, 'If I am doing my work properly surely they *must* feel good.' Carers can't change other people but they can offer conditions that will facilitate change. That's what care is about. If, when and how a client picks up the opportunity is beyond the carer's power. What is essential, though, is to offer these facilitating conditions consistently, since we never know if or when somebody will suddenly make use of them. Either way, carers must take old people as they are and try to understand them in their individual ways of experiencing. An essential aspect of care is in my view that, where necessary, people in need of care are *accompanied psychologically* (Pörtner, 2003/2007: 107–8, 206). Unfortunately, this aspect, until now, has not been paid attention to—either in the curricula of professional training programmes or in the care concepts of organisations. Why is it so important and what does it actually mean?

Psychological accompaniment

As mentioned before, one of the fundamentals of person-centred work is to start from the person's individual ways of experiencing. Experiencing includes a wide range of more or less intense feelings, sensations and reactions. Often, how a person experiences is not clearly or unambiguously comprehensible but, rather, complicated and inconsistent. Accompanying a person psychologically means grasping and reflecting this complex mental process. This is not easy, since we are more used to discussing things factually than communicating on the level of experiencing. Carers need support and orientation in becoming more sensitive in their awareness of other people's ways of experiencing and in sensibly responding to these. From this consideration originates the idea of psychological accompaniment.

How can it be helpful for old people to be accompanied psychologically? The various changes this chapter of life brings about— loss of people who are close to them; physical and mental changes; new unfamiliar circumstances, such as moving to a residence for the elderly— are not always easy to cope with. They lead to various reactions: grief, anxiety, anger, irritation, bitterness, withdrawal. Understanding and empathy for these feelings will help the people concerned to gradually accept and cope with these differences. That is why accompanying people psychologically is particularly important in helping them to readjust to a new situation.

'Psychological accompaniment' is not psychotherapy. It is not about working on unresolved conflicts, problems or aspects of biography. Of course, this might be helpful too, but it is not up to carers and not the task of psychological accompaniment—it requires counselling or psychotherapy by experienced professionals, and this option should also be available for old people if they want it. For some people it is important to review certain aspects of their lives in order to reconcile their past and to gain calm and peace for the last stretch of their road; psychotherapy or counselling can offer helpful support with this process.

To accompany a person psychologically, however, means subtly grasping and being empathic with a person's actual state of mind so that she or he will not feel left alone with it, but understood and accepted. No special 'hours' are necessary for this: on the contrary, accompanying people psychologically must be integrated into regular, everyday care in order to stimulate and reinforce their contact with how they experience. This is particularly important with people who are confused or who suffer from mental disorders. Being accompanied psychologically helps people to cope better with their internal as well as the external reality and contributes to them feeling better, to tensions diminishing and conflicts being resolved. Moreover, carers who are able to carefully accompany a person psychologically will be less at risk, through awkward reactions, to unintentionally reinforcing confusion or mental disorders.

To accompany people psychologically is a beautiful, interesting, yet at the same time very demanding task, which cannot be expected to be accomplished just 'naturally' and spontaneously. Everybody who is working in this field, regardless of professional background, should be offered the opportunity to train their sensitivity to individual ways of experiencing and to practise accompanying other people psychologically. The lack of such opportunities in training and educational programmes should be addressed as soon as possible.

This complexity of personal and professional requirements makes it clear that care for old people is a highly demanding task, even or particularly, when their mental state is declining. This task requires sensitivity and differentiation. Often it is a question of nuances left to the carers' discretion. This raises the next question.

How can the quality of person-centred work be evaluated?

This is of crucial importance as nowadays quality control is required everywhere and attached with great value. Is it at all possible to demonstrate and evaluate such personal qualities as being sensitive, interested in other people and ready to reflect and work on oneself? Some people doubt that person-centred care is possible where there is so much emphasis on quality management. This conclusion is wrong. Person-centred principles are not only perfectly compatible with quality management but also provide sensible criteria for quality control. Adequate criteria are the crucial point. Quantitative criteria (like 'how much time for which action') are not relevant for the quality of care. Criteria must encapsulate the *essential* of quality required in care. And (this is important for the motivation of staff who are often opposed to quality control) administrative duties should not take too much time and energy away from the practical work that quality control is about.

One of the most important criterion is the well-being of people in need of care. *Their* perspective is crucial for evaluating how an organisation works and must be given first priority in quality control. Until now this has been the exception rather than the rule. As an example, an institution in Switzerland, SSBL (Stiftung für Schwerbehinderte,

Luzern: Foundation for people with severe disabilities, Lucerne), developed special tools to allow the inclusion in their periodic opinion polls of people with severe mental handicaps, not able to express themselves verbally (Pörtner, 2003/2007: 77).

Analogue tools can be developed for people suffering from dementia: DCM (Dementia Care Mapping), developed by Kitwood and his Bradford Dementia Group, is an example of such a tool (Kitwood, 1997b).

Care for people with dementia is about facilitating 'relative well-being' (Kitwood & Bredin, 1992), which 'in dementia is more concerned with personhood maintained, rather than with minimising impairment. It is related to emotional experience, personality, self-esteem, creativity and other characteristics assumed to remain relatively unscathed by the disease process' (Morton, 1999: 109 & 111). A person's subjective experience is the decisive factor in her well-being, not what others consider relevant (usually aspects like cleanliness, tidiness and unobtrusive behaviour) because 'funds flow for the socially presentable' (Müller-Hergl, 2004).

However, asking if residents are content is not enough to grant quality of care. Asked such questions, people tend to give the required answers, particularly when they depend on the asking authority, and this has to be taken into account when evaluating the answers. Even subtle hints of dissatisfaction must be taken very seriously in order to find ways for improvement. Objective criteria are also necessary to assess if and how staff work with the concepts expected by the organisation. Person-centred attitude, as such, is not measurable but can be seen in what staff members are concretely doing, and this can be checked—on condition that the criteria are not concerned with mechanical actions but based on person-centred fundamentals. Such criteria can also be derived from the 'Seven principles' (*see* pp. 21–32) and from the 'Essentials for everyday work'(*see* pp. 33–48). The following boxes show some examples of such criteria. They must be worked through fully by each organisation according to its specific situation and the tasks of each person within the organisation, and must be applied to concrete aspects of everyday work.

Examples of quality control criteria based on person-centred principles

Clarity
• How clear are carers in their ways of acting and expressing themselves?
• It is not what is lacking that is important but what is there.
• Are carers able to recognise the resources of Ms. X and Mr. Y, or do they focus on her/his deficiencies, such as 'problematic behaviour', symptoms, impairments?

Self-responsibility
• In which situations are Mr. X or Ms. Y able to decide for themselves?
• Is responsibility left to him/her?

Respond to experiencing
• Do carers understand and take into account how a specific situation is experienced by Ms. X and Mr. Y?

Foster a person's own ways
• Where, specifically, do carers respect and support Mr. X's and Ms. Y's own ways?

Manageable choices
• What are the choices offered to Ms. X and Mr. Y?
• Are those sufficient? Not enough?
• Are Ms. X and Mr. Y able to manage them? Or is it too much for her/him?

Support to act independently
• What kind of support are Mr. X and Ms. Y provided with?
• Is it appropriate? Too much? Not enough?

Small steps
• Do carers perceive and acknowledge small steps of growth?
• How do they encourage the old people?
• Do they frequently reprimand them for errors and omissions?

Listen, take other people seriously, find their 'language'
• Are carers able and ready to put their own ideas aside and be open to the world of the other person?
• Do they listen accurately, or incorporate what they hear with their own ideas?

Recognise one's own part
• Are carers able and ready to reflect upon what they are doing?

6
Specific circumstances for consideration

The importance of granting a quality of care that includes professional as well as personal competence becomes even more obvious when we look at some specific circumstances of this work.

Role reversal between the generations

The people who provide care for the old are (sometimes considerably) younger than those they care for. This is in the nature of things, but not unproblematic. The former, customary, allocation of roles is now reversed. The potential for conflict that this brings is not to be underestimated.

Growing up, young people learn from their elders; in their families, at school and in their professional development. They are guided by the experience of these older people in certain aspects of life. During our early years we are determined predominantly by our elders and in many ways depend upon them. With adolescence it changes. Becoming an adult implies separating from parents, leaving school and teachers behind, taking responsibility, engaging in a job and perhaps starting a family. This process is different for each person and can be experienced in many different ways. For some, it is a fight, connected with strong emotions; for others, it happens smoothly and cautiously, step by step; some have a generally hard time removing difficulties and continue to orientate on the older generation, maybe even remaining dependent on them; some others try to avoid any confrontation by silently and unobtrusively slinking off. There are many different ways to become adult and to take responsibility for oneself; and, equally diverse, is the way young people feel towards those they have moved away from. These feelings have an influence on their general attitude towards the older generation.

In the situation of care there is a new allocation of roles. Old people depend on the younger to cope with daily life and need their support in areas they can no longer manage themselves. Now the young take the lead—though in an area unknown and with which they don't yet have experience. The roles are reversed—but not quite, because one aspect remains the same: older people are still a few steps ahead on their journey through life and they have a background of experience which those younger people don't have. It is no longer the experienced leading the inexperienced into an area they are familiar with, but the inexperienced accompanying others through a chapter of life that they themselves will get to know only much later. They might have acquired some knowledge about old age, but they lack the personal experience which would help them to better understand. It is a difficult situation for both parties.

Again, carers are challenged on a very personal level as their own experiences with parents, teachers and other determining figures of that generation come into play. How they have experienced these people, how their process of separation proceeded, what feelings it left, if and how they were able to develop new ways for certain relationships (such as with their parents)—all this influences their attitude towards the people they have to care for. Only when carers, here too, recognise their own part and are clearly aware of old feelings, fears, reservations, tendencies, aversions or reactions rooted in *their* biography can they meet old people, unbiased and without transferring onto them these old emotions. This is extremely important because certain feelings and reactions related to earlier experiences might considerably interfere with their task. Some carers might have internalised that they should never contradict older people and so will do, without question, whatever is asked of them; they cannot sufficiently discriminate and are at risk of exploitation. Others transfer rebellious feelings against their parents onto those in their care and, on principle, reject whatever comes from them. Some feel themselves superior to old people and, thinking they know better, patronise them and tell them what to do. Others are over-protective and overwhelm old people with affection and care—much more than is welcome. There are countless variations, but these few examples demonstrate how crucial it is for those working in this field to know themselves well.

For old people, this switching of roles is difficult too. Some have a hard time depending on younger people, who don't have their life experience and often don't know anything about the times that have shaped the older generation. Some people have more difficulty with this than others. Depending on the individual state of mind, of previous experience and mental flexibility, old people are more or less able, in a difficult situation, to recognise *their own part too*. Carers may facilitate this process by their attitude but they must never push, expect, or ask for it to happen. The carer's task is not to educate old people but to empathically understand how they feel and to take into account that their character has been shaped by their biography. This does not imply that carers always can or must live up to every expectation.

The tension between different demands and expectations

Old people do not always realise the high personal and professional demands carers have to cope with. Mostly, they just expect good service and see themselves as the paying guests of an organisation where they can (as in a hotel) make demands and give orders. They see the carers not so much as qualified professionals but employees who are there to help them and grant their wishes. This is, of course, not true for everybody. Many people never demand too much and appreciate what carers do; there are even those who don't ask for anything at all, but gratefully take what they receive as a gift. Though they certainly have a right to good care, they leave all responsibility to the carers and may even be too docile. Then there are those who cannot come to terms with having had to give up their home and (usually not voluntarily) move to this new place. They expect everything to continue as it was before and, as this is hardly possible, they will never be really satisfied.

The interests and expectations of different people are as individual as their personalities and biographies. Ms. L, for example, who has worked hard all her life and not had much to live on, feels in the old people's residence, 'I have never been so comfortable'. Whereas Mr. U, who in his active years was a hotel manager and used to being Head of Personnel, sees himself still in this role—much to the irritation of the staff who won't put up with it and think, with reason, that it is not up to him to manage them. Carers often feel scorned and used by residents like Mr. U; they react brusquely and so begins a vicious circle, leading nowhere and stressful for both parties. With the over-adapted, those who gratefully fall into line with everything, carers might be tempted to just accept the submissive attitude as an easy option—but then the true needs of these people will be neglected. Though it might be an understandable reaction, it will neither foster the well-being of the people concerned nor make carers feel really satisfied with their work.

To respond to high professional and personal demands on the one hand and to provide simple services on the other is a difficult equation for qualified staff. Quite rightly, they see themselves not as servants but as professionals who want to use their knowledge and skills. The old people (who, the carers believe, should appreciate that things are being done in their own interests) sometimes see it differently. They just want their wishes met—wishes that sometimes do not correspond at all with the staff's ideas about their work. Is there any possibility of finding a common denominator for these opposing expectations and demands? A first step would be to take another viewpoint. Not to see them as irreconcilable contradictions but to link them in a way that allows them to facilitate and complete each other. From this point of view, daily routine and simple services acquire a totally different status: they become instruments for using professional competence.

The art of integrating professional competence into services

This is a crucial element of care. When Ms. M asks the carer to help her find her glasses, it is an opportunity to find out how she is feeling, perhaps what she is reading or what her interests are. It is sometimes much easier to establish contact on these sorts of occasion than to deliberately try to start a conversation. Psychological accompaniment, as well as just talking with each other, can and should be integrated into daily duties. It doesn't always have to be a special conversation; on the contrary, many people are much more open and communicative in everyday situations. Washing her face, combing her hair or cutting her nails, carers can learn a lot about how Ms. F feels and what she likes. When Mr. T asks the carer to choose him a tie it might be an opportunity for him to speak of some memory of his wife. Carrying out his personal hygiene offers the carer an approach to Mr. W's way of experiencing, to what he likes or dislikes, so that this can be taken into account. Thus, contact and trust might develop.

Even when somebody asks for a help that is not really within the remit of carers, they can benefit from the opportunity to get in contact and, with this, return to one of their core tasks. Expressed desires can always be understood as opportunities for contact. Thus, being asked to do something that is not really their duty can be used by carers as vehicle for fulfilling an important task: to accompany a person's experiencing and to reinforce contact functions. There are, of course, limits to this.

Ability to discriminate

This is as much a part of professional competence as being able to empathically understand others. Carers might easily, from time to time, do Mr. F a favour that is not really part of their duty or help Ms. X with something she could just as easily do herself. However, this should not become the norm. Carers should not let themselves be used and manipulated but find a good balance between the expectations of old people and the professional demands of their work. It is indispensable for carers to be able to discriminate between themselves and their clients, where necessary, so that they take good care of themselves and don't wear themselves out. They must take their own experiencing as seriously as that of the residents—of course within the scope of their task—and be aware of their limits.

However, it depends very much on *how* such limits are communicated so that they can be accepted by the other person. Again, the best way is firstly to be empathic with how this person feels about the situation and, from there—based on acceptance and understanding—to decide one's own position. When people feel accepted and understood they are much more ready to understand others too and to respect their limits.

There is another crucial subject in this work which cannot and should not be avoided.

Death and dying

Old people in need of care are in their last stage of life, which inevitably leads to death. Even though this fact is often repressed, glossed over or ignored, it is always there in the background and has an influence on daily life and on the state of mind of everybody involved. Carers tend to avoid the issue as much as old people, sometimes even more so. The fact that the people in their care are moving towards death confronts them with their own transience and the realisation that they too will sooner or later reach this chapter of life. Younger people, for whom it still seems to be far away, usually face the situation much more naturally than those who are older and closer to their last years.

It is important to be natural in adequately responding to people in this chapter of their lives. Knowing that death is close does not mean feeling constantly sad, grave or depressed. In these latter years there can be many serene, pleasant and happy moments. To know that time is limited makes the here and now all the more precious—and some people, in old age, appreciate the present moment much more consciously than they did when they were young. They don't want to lose a moment and therefore sometimes have no patience and expect their wishes to be met immediately. Even though this is usually impossible, carers should react with understanding not disapproval. The fact that there is not much lifetime left is a challenge that old people try to cope with in their own individual ways. There are many variations: consciously preparing for life's end; being afraid; composedly waiting for death to come; maybe even looking forward to it, denying or repressing it—anything is possible.

Yet, however a person reacts to the fact of death coming closer, carers must respect it, even if they feel it should be approached differently. In care, the subject of dying must not be a taboo; it should have its space, but only in the measure and way a person wants it. The subject should neither be imposed on a person nor avoided; carers must have the perception to sense when somebody wants to talk about it; this is only possible when the carers themselves have dealt with the subject and with their own feelings about it. Conversations about death and dying require a special feeling and respect for the unknown. Nobody knows how it really is on this stretch of the road. To 'know better' or give 'good advice' is as out of place as the attempt to soothe or gloss over. The principle that 'growth is a lifelong process' might help in finding the right attitude and appreciation for each individual way of coping with this chapter in life—even though it might appear strange or inadequate. Do we know how we will feel and behave once we embark upon this part of our own journey?

Every step now is new and leads into unknown areas. The only certainty is that, at the end of the road, death is waiting. But *how* it will be, how it feels, nobody can know in advance. Not even the 'near-death experiences' often referred to, as they describe just the experience of near death but don't reveal anything about the final step. It will, for each individual, be a new and unique experience, never to be repeated. It may be threatening, painful, frightening, or perhaps peaceful, serene and gentle. Nobody knows and nobody can give another person guidance. To accomplish the last step of growth, human beings have to rely on themselves and their own resources. To be with a person can sometimes be helpful; however, it should never be imposed on anybody, but cautiously, gently and respectfully offered. It is a question of subtle nuance, which requires empathy with the inner world of other person and acceptance of their reality. The principle that 'there is more than one (my) reality' is particularly crucial in this context.

7
Different realities

What is reality? or 'How real is reality?' (Watzlawick,1976). Thinking about this question makes it easier to relate to the alternative realities of others, indispensable in care of old people, particularly those suffering from dementia.

Reality has many facets that we can't see all together at the same time. It is like a crystal that changes its appearance depending on where the light touches it and from where it is viewed. Not only are the realities of different people different from each other; each person, in the course of life, experiences different realities. As mentioned before, there are internal and external realities, which penetrate and influence each other. Stierlin (1981) discerns a 'hard' and a 'soft' reality; the soft consists of 'among others, our perceptions, interpretations, emotions and fantasies. Whereas anything that happens objectively, physically and in fact ... belongs to the "hard" reality' (Ciompi, 1982: 224). As we see, reality is neither unambiguous nor one-dimensional, nor can it be clearly defined, but is assembled from a variety of aspects. So what is reality?

Perception

Reality is closely connected with perception, and the perception of each individual is different. This is also confirmed by neurobiologists (Ansermet & Magistretti, 2004); François Ansermet states that 'any experience and any perception of a person is totally individual and therefore leaves an absolutely individual synaptic trace ... this leads to us all having different patterns of seeing the external world' (*NZZ am Sonntag*, 13.03.2005). We are, through our individual ways of perceiving, part of the reality we perceive. Moreover, what we are used to calling reality is influenced by cultural, religious, ethnic and personal factors, and not least by actual value systems. Therefore, reality inevitably looks somewhat different to each person. It is a fatal error to assume that what *I* perceive is *the* reality.

Watzlawick even declares, 'To believe that there is only one reality is the most dangerous of delusions' (1976: 7). A basic precondition for contact, relationship, living together and mutual understanding is accepting the different realities of different people. This is not always easy to realise. The further away another person's reality is from our own the harder it is to accept, particularly with people whose orientation, memory, perception or judgment is impaired, who suffer from delusions or seem to live in an 'other world'. However, a person's impairments are *a part of her reality* that must be seen and understood as a whole.

Development

We are not born with what we call 'being realistic' or reality sense; this develops during the first years of life. Newborn babies, at first, experience themselves and their environment as a unity. Slowly, the child learns that there is a difference between its own inner reality and the external reality it shares with others. 'Each child, in the first years of life, develops two different worlds of thinking, feeling and acting ... those represent two different realities' (Lempp, 2003: 36). Small children experience both realities as equally real, easily switching from one to the other and linking them together.

Example
Little Vera and her parents are visiting friends who have moved to a new house. While the adults look around, Vera stays in the living room and plays with her (imaginary) teddy bear. The adults come back and Vera's father is just about to sit in a chair when Vera screams, 'No Dad, please, the bear is sitting there!' In that moment, for her, both realities are equally real.

Lempp compares this skipping from one reality to another with the experience of adults who, leaving the cinema after an exciting film or awakening from a dream, need a moment 'in between' to return from one reality to the other (Lempp, 2003).

Growing up, the shared reality, which Lempp calls the 'main reality' (ibid.: 38), becomes more and more central, while the private reality withdraws to the background. But it is still important as a 'side reality' (ibid.) and is still, in many ways, interlaced with the 'main reality'. Even as adults, we live in different realities—dreams, daydreams, fantasies—where desires and longings periodically become true and may comfort us against pain and deception. Art too—painting, music, poetry, film—allows us to delve into other realities and go beyond the narrow limits of the everyday. Even simple television shows may serve this purpose by briefly indulging a longing for an ideal world, allowing a fantasy, offering compensation for frustration, or helping to banish fear.

These 'side' realities certainly make sense. Regression, falling back into earlier ways of experiencing, offers relief, protects people from being too stressed and allows them to distance themselves. It is extremely useful for bridging a crisis or a difficult life situation by allowing a breathing space for gathering strength to confront the problem. 'The ability to regress is an existential principle as it makes human beings capable of coping with reality' (ibid.: 80). It becomes problematic, then, only when a person can no longer discriminate between the different realities; for example, when side realities with threatening or frightening content become delusions, or fantasies are translated into actions (criminal acts, violence or sexual abuse). Not being able to return to reality (or perhaps, unconsciously, not wanting to) and remaining in this side reality is synonymous with mental illness.

Lempp explicitly does *not* want his considerations on regression to be related to dementia and mental changes in old age, 'because this process is not an active reorientation towards the psychological conditions of childhood, but an organic decline of brain functions' (ibid.: 25). However, though it certainly makes sense not to talk about active regression it doesn't necessarily imply that in old age—even though there is an organic decline—'the child in each person' (Lempp, 2003) should vanish and it is no longer true that 'human beings never can completely break away from their childhood' (ibid.: 12).

Changes due to old age should not *exclusively* be understood in terms of organic decline even though there is such a process. A person is never *just* demented. If growth is seen as a lifelong process it will be apparent that those lost capabilities may no longer be necessary, while others have become more meaningful—thoughts, memories, fantasies, dreams. What is dismissed as a 'loss of reality' might be a bridge towards that inevitable reality: death. Death is an 'other' reality—and I understand it without any esoteric touch: to turn into ashes or into earth *is* another reality. Regardless of how we imagine the 'afterwards' of what we believe or don't believe, it will be an *other reality* than the one we are living in now. It is quite possible that, on the journey to death, the internal reality will at times be more important than the external. It may be that the (unquestionable) loss of capabilities not *only* means loss but also liberation from burdens. In terms of lifelong growth, decline can also be understood as an approaching of this other reality, which will be there when human life has come to an end.

This certainly does not imply that carers should deny medical facts or give up supporting a person's existing abilities. It means they should *not just reduce* people to these facts but be aware of, and acknowledge, their inner world, even though it might appear strange and incomprehensible. Thus, carers can help to maintain the link between both realities. Carers are not sentenced to passivity and helplessness in the face of decline and dementia but can, by the quality of their care, decisively influence its process. Therefore, it is advisable 'to push the dementia to one side and allow the person to occupy the forefront of our appreciation' (Morton, 1999: 109).

Communication

We don't have to go as far as Watzlawick, who is of the opinion 'that the so-called reality is the result of communication' (Watzlawick, 1976: 7). However, communication undeniably has a determining influence on what we perceive as reality.

As mentioned before, internal and external realities are intertwined and influence each other; the internal reality of a person is determined not only by the attitudes of those in their environment but also by intra-psychological and organic factors. Neurological impairments should not be ignored or denied, but seeing those people *exclusively* from this perspective has disastrous consequences.

Since 1987, Tom Kitwood has constantly emphasised this, and the experiences of Bell and McGregor at the Spring Mount Residential Home in Bradford (also founded in 1987) prove that there *are* other ways and that the personhood of people with dementia does not inevitably get lost but can be preserved by a milieu that offers adequate care (Bell & McGregor, 1994, 1995). This confirms Kitwood's conviction that just acting from the perspective of neuropathology is not only inadequate but extremely damaging.

When Kitwood referred to the 'malignant social psychology', he was pointing to a set of characteristic aspects of interpersonal interactions and relationships which are perceived as damaging to the personhood of the person with dementia. In another of Kitwood's models for understanding dementia, MSP is held to be one of the factors which combine in a 'dialectical relationship' with neurological impairment to produce senile dementia. (Morton, 1999: 106)

It is 'seldom created as a result of malicious intent. Rather, it is part of the cultural inheritance of dementia care' (Morton, 1999: 108). The exclusively neuropathological view has fostered the belief that dementia 'leaves behind a "shell" of a person' and that how carers 'relate to this person matters little as their deterioration is inevitable and they are no longer present anyway' (Morton, 1999: 100). Although, in the meantime, much has changed for the better, this opinion is still widespread, including amongst carers, particularly when they are poorly or inadequately trained and ignorant of how much they can, positively or negatively, influence the process of dementia by the way they relate to the person.

Disregarding their subjective reality forces human beings into isolation, with the effect that they increasingly lose contact with common reality. The more they withdraw the less they are understood, and the less they feel understood the more they withdraw—a vicious circle which continuously reinforces itself. This should not be. On the contrary, care should stimulate and reinforce contact with common reality. This is possible only when the subjective reality of a person is also acknowledged and taken seriously. The two levels of reality must not be cut off from each other by only accepting one of them. A person who feels that her internal reality is respected will be much more capable of also perceiving external reality. Carers can foster and support this ability by building bridges between the different aspects of reality. For this, Prouty's pre-therapeutic approach offers, with contact reflections (*see* p. 17), a methodical instrument that is precious in two ways: contact reflections open a door to the inner world of others while at the same time helping these people to get in contact with the reality around them.

Dreams

We all know 'that other reality' of dreams. In dreams, a part of us becomes visible which, when we are awake, is hidden or only fragmentarily accessible in our remembrance of the dream. In our dreams we live in another world, closely connected with the one familiar to us when awake but quite differently put together. This inner world has its own colours and images and follows its own timing and laws. It is the other side of our experiencing, inactive in our waking state. Regardless of the meaning attributed to its content—throughout history there have been, and still are, very different opinions about this—dreaming is an intra-psychological process with the purpose of emotional processing. Since the first observations of REM sleep by Aserinsky and Kleitmann (1953), we have known that all human beings regularly dream, including those who believe they never do. Recent research sees 'the higher function of dreams in developing, maintaining (regulation) and restitution of psychological organisation' (Fosshage, 2000: 721), Awaking from a dream, in this strange state of being between two worlds, not there anymore but not quite here yet either, when we briefly float on two levels of reality, flowing together for a moment—in this moment, we clearly experience that there is *more than one reality.*

In the past, I have been mainly interested in the content of my dreams and, waking up, have tried to remember them. Nowadays, it is more the sensation of coming from a totally different reality that I dwell on for a moment when I wake and I sometimes ask myself if it could be that the reality of the dream is, in some way, creating a psychological link to that other reality that life inevitably leads to: the reality of death and dying. The idea is somehow comforting, even though it might spring from an unconscious wish to give shape to the unimaginable. However, from the point of view of 'development, maintenance (regulation) and restitution of psychological organisation' (ibid.), it doesn't seem an unreasonable idea, since the issue of death and dying becomes increasingly significant the older we get.

It is quite possible that states of confusion and disorientation, even when due to neurophysiologic impairments, are experienced in a similar way to dreams and, like those, have a function. We do not know, but there are indications suggesting it. For example, many people speak of the quite unexpected moments of intense emotional presence they have experienced with relatives who have, to a great extent or even totally, lost their intellectual and practical abilities.

Example

Mr. S, who had always had a difficult relationship with his very intellectual and dominating mother, felt that there were moments during the last days before she died that were the most beautiful he had ever had with her.

Even though, or perhaps because, she had reached the state they had both always feared, when everything she represented had fallen away from her, he felt an extraordinary and deeply emotional connection between them.

Comparison with dreams also helps carers to be more understanding and relaxed towards states of confusion and consequent strange behaviour in old people, and to accept these things as part of their reality rather than blaming them. When carers are aware of how manifold reality is, they will inevitably see their own as a little more relative and develop a broader understanding towards others. This is an excellent precondition for offering individual approaches and high quality in the care of old people.

8
Looking to the future

How people think they will live into old age has changed—and so have demands on care. There is no *one* right way to live the final years of one's life and there are almost as many ways of envisaging old age as there are people, but one thing is indisputable: a flexibility in care that responds to individual needs is essential. The changes that have occurred in the last few decades have resulted from both demographic development and social change; the increasing numbers of old people, at least in the populations of Western Europe, have become a political and economic factor, valued both in the positive economic terms of spending power and the negative costs to social services.

A broad spectrum of demands

Most old people nowadays bear little resemblance to those of times past, when being old (before the state pension and for those without a personal fortune) meant being poor and grateful for welfare and charity. These days we are more likely to be dealing with self-confident personalities who know exactly what they want and what they are entitled to. Pension entitlement is, for the time being, taken for granted with no certainty that it can be protected in the future, although those who contributed to the prosperity of the decades after World War II know how to defend their rights (for example, the 'Gray Panthers', a German organisation for senior citizens). The rebellious generation of 'baby boomers' is also approaching retirement and is unlikely to be docile or 'easy-care'; their desires and needs will be as diverse as their origins, experiences, life conditions and biographies. Future care will require a wide spectrum of services to satisfy an increasing variety of demands.

According to opinion polls, most people would prefer to stay in a familiar environment as long as possible; in their own home or at least in their same neighbourhood. This will require increasingly flexible services and residential options, such as warden-controlled flats, purpose-built apartments, and nursing homes for people with dementia that will grant them 'relative well-being'.

Promising new approaches, but only tentative implementation

There is a dawning realisation in organisations and institutions for the old that these people can no longer be treated in the customary way. Many changes have taken place in the past few years, some of them positive. But whilst there are progressive concepts focusing on individuality and well-being, there are also hopelessly inadequate systems still being used. Conflicting messages within society, institutions and even conflicting needs within individual people all contribute to the maintenance of the status quo. Equally, there are well-educated, motivated carers open to new ideas whilst others are entrenched in outdated opinion and rigid tradition; there are old people who are self-confident, interested and well informed and there are those who believe that life is over when its former mainstays—families, partnerships, jobs—are no longer there. They give up their own desires and needs and submit to whatever they are offered, indirectly contributing to further entrenchment and impeding necessary change; they serve the pretext of letting everything go on as before because 'people don't want anything else'.

Moreover, an evolution just begun is, in many places, already being slowed by economic constrictions. That these might be necessary is not to be disputed here, but measures are frequently taken in the wrong place and miss their point. In times of limited funds it is particularly important to be careful with existing human and financial resources and to use them *sensibly.* More than ever, care has to concentrate on what is essential. Erosive power struggles, arrogant, superior attitudes, and authoritarian attempts to impose upon old people something they don't want are an irresponsible waste of energy, human labour and therefore economic resources. As a consequence, these vital resources are not available for other important aspects of care. The well-being of residents contributes to the satisfaction of the carer's work. People who find themselves taken seriously and who are, within the limits of their capabilities, given autonomy and self-responsibility, are more balanced, more content, have fewer problems and are therefore less likely to create stress for their carers. Staff who are relaxed and motivated work better, are less often sick and burned out, and thus create a positive economic effect.

The Spring Mount example shows 'that good quality dementia care can achieve far more than was previously imagined' (Morton, 1999: 138). Bell and McGregor don't deny the cognitive deficiencies of their residents but while the care environment

> ... acknowledges that disabilities, especially in the areas of memory, communication and practical skills are very real and require compensatory action by staff, residents remain in control of their social situation and in charge of how they spend their day. Staff do not interfere in interactions between residents, even if they become hostile, nor do they exert control over residents with aspects of their daily routine, such as bed-times. Staff are encouraged to develop deeper interpersonal relationships with residents, acknowledging their losses and facilitating adjustment, exploration and development. (Morton, 1999: 137–8)

These remarkable principles are, unfortunately, still far from being adopted by the majority of institutions in most countries. Despite its undeniable success, the example of Spring Mount has yet to become universally accepted. Outdated practices and ossified structures die surprisingly slowly, even in organisations that aspire to better ideals. Systems are there to serve people, not vice versa—this is a truism often pronounced but rarely consistently realised. However, clear indicators have been pointing the way for a long time. More than twenty years ago, Erich Grond showed the extent to which confusion is influenced by social-psychological and institutional factors and how the relationship with the carers is, therefore, of crucial importance (Grond, 1984).

The approach developed by Tom Kitwood with the Bradford Dementia Group has had a far-reaching impact in Britain and initiated considerable improvements in dementia care. However, here too, many organisations still ignore the findings and remain trapped in a strictly medical model. In German-speaking countries, since being published in German, Kitwood's work has received increasing attention; in particular, his method of evaluation, 'Dementia Care Mapping' (Kitwood, 1997b), 'is widely known and occasionally applied' (Müller-Hergl, 2003). The approach is mainly conveyed through training courses and, more or less thoroughly, transferred by participants to their institutions. But, 'Without the patient insistence of some people in charge, positive beginnings that had been initiated with much effort, due to lack of firm foundation, break down with alarming rapidity' (Müller-Hergl, 2003). This is true for a number of innovative models deriving from person-centred principles.

'These instruments, despite being widely known, are very rarely anchored in practice. For a person with dementia to find a place to live in a milieu offering person-centred care, is still a exceptional stroke of luck' (ibid.).

However, it is an important step forward that these innovative concepts have become part of various training programmes. In time, a new generation of carers will evolve who feel committed to a humanistic view of care and nursing. This is bound to have a positive influence on the institutions where they work. But while staff members who have participated in training programmes may, by their influence, achieve improvements here and there, and sometimes even initiate a general change, such individual initiatives can also produce negative effects— particularly if they are not explicitly supported by the management, or if other staff members feel left out and therefore boycott the proposed changes. There is also the danger that a single (sometimes very short and often superficial) workshop or seminar will not have given participants sufficient practical skill and may lack proper grounding in the underpinning principles. Also, certain aspects of a method will be picked out and rashly applied; this is unlikely to be productive, as the carer's focus is not on the person but on the method. Methods—detached from person-centred principles—are often misunderstood as easy 'techniques', or some particularly catchy theoretical consideration is taken out of context and adopted as 'the truth'—without detailed examination of whether it really does apply to *this* person and *this* situation. Professionals too often forget that the point of theoretical constructs is *to understand,* not to judge, human beings.

Theories are tools for understanding, not 'the truth'

It cannot be emphasised too much that theories are *approaches* to a better understanding of other people, *not absolute truths*. When we hold on too tightly to theory to explain unusual or incomprehensible behaviour, we risk missing the person. The essential concept is always *this person in his uniqueness.* Carers must never forget this, as tempting as it might be, because it is so hard to endure what is not clearly comprehensible.

The original approach of Naomi Feil, for example, offered a forward-looking perspective. But some of the theories she later developed—such as the four stages of dementia, or the assumption that, in the last stage, anything a person expresses refers to the past, or her fixed interpretations of body language—are not beyond doubt and cannot be adopted uncritically. Ian Morton (1999) presents a highly competent and differentiated critical study asking the necessary questions and expressing well-founded doubts whilst at the same time explicitly pointing to Feil's merits and the precious stimulus she represented for dementia care. He also has reservations about some of Kitwood's ideas that in no way diminish the outstanding significance of his work.

Care is about human beings, not methods

Within the last few years, several valuable and helpful methods have been developed which are perfectly compatible with the person-centred attitude. There are many other approaches, besides those of Feil and Kitwood—including the integration of painting, music, dancing and other activities. But no method, however good it might be, should become an end in itself. Unfortunately, this happens quite frequently. Carers often forget that methods are *just tools* to support person-centred principles. Instead of the constant application of a method, we must always ask: is the method compatible with these principles and appropriate *in this situation and with this person?* It is not *that* the method is used but *how* it is used that is paramount.

Example

A video shows how nursing home staff work with biographic methods. The family of Ms. S is asked to bring along some of the photos she has collected during her life. In a detailed conversation with family members the carer tries to find out about the pictures; who they are of and when and where they were taken. Then she carefully prepares a picture album using those which the relatives think, or she herself believes, to be particularly meaningful to Ms. S. The next sequence shows the carer, together with Ms. S, looking through the album. She comments on certain pictures, 'This was your wedding was it?', or asks questions about places and people. Ms. S answers obligingly but clearly isn't particularly interested. What she really does seem to enjoy, though, is the carer's attention. However, the conversation is predominantly about what the carer is interested in—and this should not be the aim.

The example shows the importance of *how* a method is applied and that it is very much a matter of nuance. In other words, the fundamental principles accepted by the carer determine how the method will be enacted; so, in principle, the photo album is a good idea. However, the album itself is not as important as its purpose: to stimulate memories in Ms. S and to allow her to share them—if she wants to. The carer could have served this purpose much better by doing the album *together with*

Ms. S instead of spending so much time questioning family members and then compiling it herself. Had she done this, Ms. S would have gained what she obviously most appreciates: the time and attention of the carer. Compiling the album of memories *with* her, *not for* her, would have meant really taking her seriously. *She* is the expert on her memories, not the carer and not the family. Memories might have arisen through quite different pictures than those chosen by the family and it wouldn't have mattered if the album had been less orderly and complete. The memories that are meaningful to Ms. S *now* are the essential thing. And there is another aspect—given the frequent complaint that carers have less and less time for the old people—doing it this way allows the carer to conserve her time and energy and use it more sensibly.

It is not enough to apply a method just because it is good: it has to be embedded in person-centred principles, so the status given to these principles within institutions is of major importance.

Establishing a person-centred culture

It is not only a 'new culture of dementia care' (Kitwood, 1997a) that needs to evolve but, in a much more general sense, a *new culture of dealing with old age and old people:* person-centred principles offer a solid foundation for this. These are best achieved by working consistently (on the basis of the principles and concepts described in this book) within the framework of a *person-centred culture* that has been established *in the whole institution*—with the whole staff at every area and level, including board and management, working according to the same principles.

A person-centred programme, clearly supported by the management and obligatory for everybody, facilitates continuity and staff orientation by defining a structure within which there is freedom to use individual capabilities and resources. In an institution where work is consistently oriented on person-centred principles—by the whole staff—a person-centred culture will eventually develop. Innovative stimuli, which individuals bring back from workshops, will fall on fertile ground and be easily integrated—as long as they are in harmony with this culture. Thus, those inappropriate experiments, which unnecessarily use up the goodwill and energy of the carers and residents, can be avoided.

The seven principles (*see* pp. 21–32) and the essentials of everyday care (*see* pp. 33–48) create a structure offering
- *the staff* clear guidelines for achieving a person-centred attitude in their daily work;

- *job applicants* detailed information about what is expected from them, helping them to decide whether or not they want to work in this organisation;
- *the residents* a consistent quality of care to be expected equally from all staff members;
- *the management* preconditions for defining adequate and sensible quality criteria.

However, whilst a person-centred culture fully anchored in an organisation or institution is desirable, this cannot always be immediately achieved. This raises the question ...

Are partial solutions to be recommended too?

In big organisations, where extensive changes are more difficult to implement, it is not always immediately possible to introduce a new concept throughout the whole institution. Here, it makes sense to start person-centred work gradually, perhaps in a specific section or ward, where the experience gained will later help to spread the concept to other sections of the organisation.

Whether person-centred principles are adopted by the whole organisation or, initially, only by certain sections, it is important that staff can rely on being supported by the management and that the programme is introduced carefully. A detailed consideration of the person-centred concept, its implications for management and the different approaches of two organisations for people with special needs, can be found in *Trust and Understanding* (Pörtner, 1996/2007: 63–77). The following point is of crucial importance ...

Systems must support, not inhibit

It is essential that the structure and philosophy of an organisation are not poles apart. Structures are not there for their own sake but to serve the goals and purposes of the organisation. They must prepare the way for the implementation of the philosophy and principles of the organisation to be committed to statute and create a favourable working atmosphere. Of course, a structure must also optimise an organisation's progress— but always within the remit of core tasks, not as an end in itself.

Example

On their day of departure from the (otherwise very comfortable) guesthouse of a conference centre, guests are asked to vacate their rooms before breakfast. This creates an uncomfortable prospect: where will they brush their teeth afterwards? It is understandable that the rooms must be ready in good time for new guests but, since check-in is not until 4 p.m. and most guests will still be participating in a conference starting at 9.00 a.m. they could easily vacate their rooms between breakfast and then. The rooms can't be cleaned all at the same time and some are invariably vacated earlier anyway, but the duty manager will not budge on the issue, saying 'That's impossible, the rooms have to be made ready one after the other in the correct order!'

This is a trivial but illustrative example of how systems can miss their point completely. In this case, the rule is nothing but a harassing imposition on the guests for whom the guesthouse ought, in any case, to be available. If the needs of the guests are ignored in the guesthouse, how are people treated in the facilities for people with special needs run by the same organisation?

Of course, organisations must ensure that work proceeds as smoothly as possible, but this should not conflict with their overall objective. Residents being served dinner as early as five p.m. and then given nothing to eat until breakfast is still a widespread and bad practice in homes for the elderly, even though it has long been recognised that low blood sugar levels result in a state of confusion in old people (*see* p. 40)—a situation that benefits nobody. 'In a residential home where, as a result of this recognition, the residents were provided with late night and early morning snacks, there were, after six months, twenty five per cent less confused people!' (Grond, 1984/1992: 78). With a little goodwill and clever organisation solutions can easily be found and implemented.

The variety of different needs also requires *flexibility* with meal and bedtimes. Of course, there must be a basic daily schedule that people who need regularity can rely upon. But it should represent just a *framework* that leaves some *leeway* for individual requirements. If somebody has been lying awake half the night and wants to sleep through the morning, this should be possible. Following the rhythm of their body is particularly important for old people in taking care of their health and strength. Institutions should not inhibit this with strict regulations but offer support within a flexible framework. With the technical aids at our disposal nowadays and a little talent for organisation this should not be a problem; what prevents it is long-established habit and entrenched ideas. The experiences at Spring Mount provide impressive evidence that there are other and better ways. But there is one aspect that is fundamental to both the individual well-being of old people and the future development of care.

Attitudes to old age

Well-being and contentment in old age depend not only on external circumstances but also on the attitude of people themselves.

Example

On a walk I meet 85-year-old Ms. C, who I have not seen for some time as she has been ill. To my question, how is she doing now, she answers: 'Excellent—I enjoy life.' Ms. C used to be a musician but had to give up playing the violin some years ago due to her increasingly poor hearing. She tells me she has had to reduce her activities because she needs so much sleep and everything now goes much more slowly. These days she just has enough time to take care of her house, which she still does herself. She lives alone with a cat and is quite happy with her life. 'Life begins at eighty' she declares, laughing.

For 79-year-old Ms. A, things are quite different. Her husband died a few years ago at the age of 93 and she still bemoans her fate, feeling that she has been wronged. Although she is in good health and always out doing things, she is not really able to enjoy anything because she always makes unfavourable comparisons, finding that everything used to be much nicer when her husband was alive.

These are two quite different attitudes towards life's changes and they have a huge influence on how a person feels. Many old people have, themselves, a negative attitude towards ageing and thus reduce their well-being even more. However, it is not the carer's job to correct or reprimand but, with an open mind and no hint of judgementalism, to help those in their care to feel more positive. To be met with respect and positive regard increases self-esteem and helps the old towards a less negative view of themselves and the changes brought about by old age.

A person's attitude doesn't only influence their own state of mind. The way society in general views old age finds expression in the way it cares for its elderly and this in turn influences how *they* feel. It is a cycle influenced by the attitude of every single person—including every carer and all those needing care.

Peter Gross, Professor of Sociology at the University of St. Gallen, Switzerland suggests: 'It is not the fact of ageing that gives cause for concern, but the way we deal with it' (Gross, 2004). Here we see that, slowly, change *is* occurring. The experience and wisdom of age is beginning to be in demand again. It will no longer be taken for granted

that everyone aspires to early retirement and, already, some early retirees
(even those who before had more or less been forced to retire to make
way for younger people) are being re-employed as consultants by their
former employers. Indeed, some new voices talk of the *opportunities*
implicit in age and an ageing population. Thomas Straubhaar, Professor
of Economics at the University of Hamburg, Germany, for example,
thinks that the decreasing birth rate offers the prospect of more space:
smaller classes, less crowded lecture halls, less congested roads. He
points to the fact that more space implies more time: teachers will have
more time for their students, there will be fewer traffic jams, shorter
queues etc. (interview at Television SWR, Germany, 18.11.2004). For
Peter Gross, ageing Western societies play an important role for cultures
with younger populations in that they counterbalance 'the young,
offensive evolutions with the values of an old culture' (conversation
with O.J, *St. Galler Tagblatt*, 25.2.2004). Slowly recognition is dawning
that growth cannot be the solution of all problems nor only goal for a
society to aim at.

However, it asks us to shift our thinking if we want the society's
ageing and shrinking population to be not only a disadvantage but also a
benefit. In the long term, old age cannot remain 'a more and more
prolonged period of late freedom and leisure, but must to some degree
include working' (*Neue Zürcher Zeitung*, 24.12.2004). Opportunites for
early retirement will drastically diminish and the prolonging of our
working life will no longer be a taboo. Flexible working hours, adapted
to the specific conditions of older people, will be necessary because
'physical strength decreases, experience and (social) competences
increase' (Straubhaar, 1993). Certain impairments of age, such as
forgetfulness and slowness, should not automatically be equated with
incompetence but taken into consideration. They can, to some degree, be
compensated for with adequate organisational and technical aids.

We need a 'new culture of ageing in order to make better use of the
competences of older people' suggests Peter Gross (interview at the
'Tages-Anzeiger', Zürich, 15.04.2004). However, he also reminds us that
'specific solutions have to be worked out for the different professional
fields' (Gross, 2004). Of course, there is a difference between working,
say, in an office, in a job one likes, and hard physical labour. There needs
to be a variety of solutions appropriate to individual choices. It is even
possible that people in need of care could still do certain jobs even when
living in a residential facility. Some residents might find this preferable
to simply being offered distractions or forms of entertainment. Of course,
it would have to be an activity acceptable to them, that they are interested

in and find meaningful. Moreover, it must be one of several options, never obligatory or the 'norm'.

The effects of such developments on people suffering from dementia are hard to predict. Will they be pushed even further into the cold? Or, conversely, could a new culture of ageing be beneficial to them too, perhaps even result in a decrease in dementia by allowing old people a more prolonged use of their resources, thus making them feel more part of society? Both are possible. But we must not allow two classes of old age to develop, or an increasing gap to open up between the 'young old', who are still integrated, and others who have more or less given up. If we work in accordance with what has been learned, the expectation that dementia will result in the decay of personality will cease to be a forgone conclusion. Adequate care can provide 'relative well-being' (Kitwood & Bredin, 1992) for people with dementia. And we should never forget that the person who is physically and mentally capable at seventy, at eighty, might fall ill with dementia—and that regardless of how much this might change and disable him or her, in their core they will remain the person they always were, and this must be taken seriously.

It is undeniable that people can change considerably in old age. In people who suffer from dementia the changes are sometimes so drastic that they become hard to reach; strangers to those who knew them before. Yet to conclude that they are no longer sentient beings is a fatal error and ethically irresponsible.

Nobody can know in advance if and how a person is going to change.

Example
Ms. J and her friend Ms. E are discussing nursing homes. Ms. J says that, for her, the worst thing would be having to share a room with someone else. Ms. E, who works in a nursing home, disagrees, 'Once you have dementia you won't care any more.' Ms. J vigorously denies this, insisting that her feelings will never change.

In some ways they are both right. We know from experience that people's tastes can suddenly become completely different or, more commonly, they can find that what they used to detest or consider important no longer matters to them. There are others, though, whose feelings *don't* change, who still have the same likes and dislikes, still prefer classical music to pop—or vice versa. We should not insist that things will always remain the same but be open to growth and change being a lifelong process. Carers must also remain open to the feelings of people with dementia and not assume that they know how it is for them. It is different for each person and, even when somebody is no longer able to say what is pleasant or unpleasant, there will be signs. A grimace, blinking, the trace of a smile, a tense expression, a sigh—all these suggest how this person might feel. So it is important for carers to find the other person's 'language' and never to assume that human beings no longer feel anything just because they can no longer express themselves in the usual way.

In our attitude towards the old, the process of ageing and the disabilities and diseases of age, each and every one of us participates in decisions about the quality of life and care offered, not only to the old people (including those suffering from dementia) of the present generation, but also to our future selves.

9

Being old is different ... for people with mental disabilities too

Many of the experiences and insights from my work with people with mental disabilities have proved helpful in other contexts and have slipped into this book, and many ideas developed here are equally valuable in the care of people with disabilities, so a few thoughts about *their* ageing will close the circle.

Demographic development has made a significant impact on organisations for people with special needs as the life expectancy of their clients has increased remarkably. Many communities and homes were founded thirty or forty years ago in a movement to remove those with mental disabilities from psychiatric clinics and people admitted to these organisations were assured lifelong residency, but now that many of them have reached old age their environment is no longer appropriate. Some (though by no means enough) organisations have since then created special units where their older residents can live together as a group.

More facilities responding to the needs of old age must be provided for people with mental disabilities. Whilst housing them together in homogeneous groups is *one* option, there needs to be a wider choice for old people that complies with the wishes of most for more quiet, making it possible for the disabled to live their last years peacefully, in their own individual way, and allowing them to choose their own daily routine where preferred.

Example
In the homes of Mariaberg, S. Germany, thirty-two residents with mental disabilities, including some elderly, live in one, two or three-roomed flats in the grounds (in buildings formerly inhabited by employees). They are free to structure their days as they wish, but carers are available at certain times so they can get help if they need it. They can prepare their own meals or take advantage of the meal service. For those who are still working, the workshops are close by.

This approach has broad potential and substantiates my view that even within bigger organisations it is possible to implement innovative forms of living that allow more self-responsibility and freedom (Pörtner, 2003: 74–9). It offers the advantage of familiar surroundings and continued contact with friends and staff without the risk of isolation that can be imposed by a 'normal' residential block, where people with disabilities do not always become as fully integrated as the projects (based on the theoretical assumption that this sort of accommodation would facilitate a more 'normal' life) anticipated or intended. The advantage of the approach in the example above is that people can fall back on the organisation for advice and support and use the services whenever things become overwhelming. Such flexible conditions are ideal for those who no longer want to live in a group with much younger people or to uproot and move to a totally new environment.

But such opportunities are rare and many old people still live in ill-matched groups with younger residents who have completely different needs and interests; unsurprisingly, this is a frequent cause of conflict. In some cases, the older residents might feel they are getting less than their fair share because the younger people are more assertive in their demands; on the other hand, the old are sometimes quite intolerant and tyrannical towards the young. Carers should take countermeasures to reconcile both sides, using their own tolerance as an example. It is quite natural that most carers find this easier with the younger residents who are closer in age to themselves.

Example

Ms. F can never get a word in edgeways when the group is together. She has difficulty speaking and needs time to say certain words. All the others are considerably younger, talk loudly and animatedly to each other and pay no attention to Ms. F. In any case, they can't relate to what she says: to them, it is just incomprehensible 'old stuff', far removed from their experience. Ms. F feels hurt and rejected, withdraws more and more and becomes increasingly resentful towards the other residents. She meets them ill-naturedly and her challenging behaviour gets worse.

In this situation, carers should intervene and moderate, making sure that Ms. F gets a chance to speak, leading by example and showing an interest in what she says. People with mental disabilities, like anyone else, suffer when nobody is interested in what they think, feel and experience. That's why it is so important for carers to take seriously whatever a person expresses. They should never jump to the conclusion that something that seems improbable, or is unknown to them, is crazy or made up just because it stems from a person with a mental disability.

Example

Mr. N, who grew up in Schaffhausen, a Swiss city located on the right bank of the Rhine, repeatedly talks about how the city was bombed in World War II, when he was a child. As Switzerland didn't participate in the war, nobody believes him. Carers respond with, 'You just dreamt it', 'You don't believe *that* do you?', 'That's impossible'. This actual historic event—caused by the error of American bomber pilots who had learned that the Rhine was the border between Germany and Switzerland and ignored this local exception—has been forgotten and is unknown to most young people. Everybody agrees that Mr. N is making it up. Mr. N is upset and there are constant disputes about the issue. One day he tells the therapist, who is about his age, how hurt he feels by the young carers who don't believe him or take him seriously. What a relief and satisfaction to hear the therapist confirm that he can also well remember the great sensation that this event caused in his childhood!

The needs of people with mental disabilities, too, change with age. Some like their daily routine to remain constant, while many others prefer to follow their own rhythm, need more time to themselves and want to live more quietly. Like any other old person, they have the right to do so and should not be inhibited by intransigent systems. Instead, sensible individual solutions must be found.

Example

Sixty-eight-year-old Ms. S lives in sheltered housing with a woman friend. Her friend, who is a few years older, stays at home during the day while Ms. S goes to a day centre where she does pottery, which she thoroughly enjoys. However, in the morning, the two women tend to linger over breakfast, chatting cosily—but the friend always delays Ms. S, making her late and upsetting the others. 'How come she gets the same money as us even though she's always late?' they ask, as they greet her with reproaches each morning. The atmosphere is tense and the team in conflict. It doesn't actually matter if Ms. S is a bit late, but it is understandable that the others find it unfair. The staff consider different options; reducing the pay is out of question—it is already quite modest. Then it occurs to them: What would the situation be for sixty-eight-year-old *without* a mental handicap? They would be retired, not having to work. They announce that Ms. S has retired and is attending the day centre voluntarily, so she doesn't have to be there at a fixed time. This seems plausible to the others. Mr. L, who is also of pensionable age, realises he could do the same but doesn't want to. The others are all younger, regular workers and realise that they must, of course, still turn up on time. After this has been agreed, the atmosphere immediately improves. Ms. S is no longer greeted with reproaches but welcomed when she drifts in and—surprise!—she is often even a little earlier now.

This is exactly what 'comparing with normality' means (Pörtner, 2000/2007: 25–6): not trying to change people with mental disabilities to what we consider 'normal' or making unreasonable demands on them, but asking from time to time, 'How would the same situation look to someone who's not disabled?' This starting point of 'normality' can lead to a more sensible solution, appropriate to individual disability and potential.

But providing adequate residential and day facilities for people with mental disabilities when they are old is not enough; they must be accompanied and supported much earlier in their ageing process to help them better understand and accept the changes they perceive in themselves. Working together with the person concerned, a future move can be carefully prepared and the best individual solution found.

This is already a matter of concern for many carers who realise that their working practices are not doing justice to older residents. Those who are young themselves are naturally more familiar with the needs of young residents. The difficult task of accompanying people through a stage of life that carers have not yet experienced themselves is even more challenging for those working with the mentally disabled. Special-needs training, as a rule, focuses predominantly on fostering the education and personal development of younger clients. Programmes conceived for defining and achieving developmental goals (and about which there are some justified reservations anyway, *see* Hähner, Niehoff, Sack & Walther, 1998; Pörtner, 2000, 2003), for example, are totally inappropriate for the elderly. It can also be difficult for carers to discern whether certain impairments are due to the original disability or are a sign of old age—and these can become apparent at different times in different people, tending to be a little earlier in those with mental disabilities. Carers frequently interpret forgetfulness as laziness and reprimand without considering that forgetfulness is common for most of us in old age.

The transformations brought about by old age, and the issues that shape the last years, are as relevant to people with disabilities as anyone else. The fact that death is approaching often preoccupies them, even though they might not express this directly. Like anybody else, they have to cope with physical and mental changes, and it is not made easier by a 'handicapped self-concept' (Pörtner, 2003/2007: 49–52). Many people become frightened when their already limited capabilities diminish; they experience it, once more, as a failure and confirmation of the stigma 'I am disabled.' This reinforces anew the feeling of being incapable and inferior, so common among people with disabilities. Sensible care can— and must—oppose this and make it easier for people to accept the infirmities of old age as a natural part of life. Carers must help people to find ways of compensating for lost abilities or, where this is not possible, provide the necessary support.

How people cope with ageing is to a large extent influenced by what they have experienced during their lives and by how they have been cared for. In an organisation where work is based on the concepts of 'Trust and Understanding' (Pörtner, 2000/2007), where a person-centred culture has developed and where residents (not only when they are old) have choices, can take responsibility for themselves and are accompanied psychologically, there is a good chance of ageing in 'relative well-being'. In other words, how young people with mental disabilities are cared for *now* will have a direct influence on how they later cope with being old. Carers who work in a person-centred way, who respect and support the individuality of people with mental disabilities and are open to the 'otherness' of other people, are well prepared to offer their clients appropriate care as they age. Moreover, they may become more sensitive to the 'otherness' that their own old age will bring and thus, perhaps, be able to anticipate it with more confidence.

References

Ansermet, F & Magistretti, P (2004) *À Chacun son Cerveau. Plasticité neuronale et inconscient*. Paris: Odile Jacob.

Aserinsky, E & Kleitman, N (1953) Regularly occurring periods of eye motility, and concomitant phenomena, during sleep. *Science, 118*, 273–4.

Bachmann, I (1953) *Die Gestundete Zeit. Gedichte*. München: Piper.

Bell, J & McGregor, I (1994) Breaking free from myths that restrain us. *Journal of Dementia Care, 2* (4), 14–15.

Bell, J & McGregor, I (1995) A challenge to stage theories of dementia. In T Kitwood & S Benson (Eds) *The New Culture of Dementia Care* (pp. 12–14). London: Hawker Publications.

Ciompi, L (1982) *Affektlogik*. Stuttgart: Klett-Cotta. (5th edn, 1998).

Feil, N (1982) *Validation: The Feil Method*. Cleveland: Feil Productions. (2nd revised edn, 1992).

Feil, N (1993) *The Validation Breakthrough*. Cleveland: Health Professions Press.

Fosshage, JL (2000) Traum, Traumdeutung. In G Stumm & H Pritz (Eds) *Wörterbuch der Psychotherapie*. Wien: Springer.

Grond, E (1984) *Die Pflege verwirrter alter Menschen. Psychisch Alterskranke und ihre Helfer im menschlichen Miteinander*. Freiburg i. Br.: Lambertus. (7th revised edn, 1992).

Gross, P (2004) Die Schweiz darf ruhig altern. In *St. Galler Tagblatt*, 17 Feb.

Hähner, U, Niehoff, U, Sack, R & Walther, H (1998) *Vom Betreuer zum Begleiter. Eine Neuorientierung unter dem Paradigma der Selbstbestimmung*. Marburg: Lebenshilfe-Verlag.

Irblich, D (1999) Gewalt und geistige Behinderung. *Geistige Behinderung, 2*, 132–45.

Kitwood, T (1997a) *Dementia Reconsidered*. Buckingham: Open University Press.

Kitwood, T (Ed) (1997b) *Evaluating Dementia Care: The DCM Method* (7th edn). Bradford: Bradford Dementia Group.

Kitwood, T & Bredin, K (1992) Towards a theory of dementia care: Personhood and well being. *Ageing and Society, 12*, 269–87.

Lempp, R (2003) *Das Kind im Menschen. Über Nebenrealitäten und*

Regression - oder: Warum wir nie erwachsen werden. Stuttgart: Klett-Cotta.

Morton, I (1999) *Person-Centred Approaches to Dementia Care.* Bicester: Winslow Press.

Müller-Hergl, C (2003) Nachwort zu T. Kitwood. *Demenz.* Bern: Hans Huber.

Müller-Hergl, C (2004) Dementia Care Mapping. Wahrnehmen und Beschreiben. *Dr. med. Mabuse, 29* (152), 37–40.

Pörtner, M (1994):*Praxis der Gesprächspsychotherapie. Interviews mit Therapeuten.* Stuttgart: Klett-Cotta.

Pörtner, M (1996) *Ernstnehmen, Zutrauen, Verstehen: Personzentrierte Haltung im Umgang mit geistig behinderten und pflegebedürftigen Menschen.* Stuttgart: Klett-Cotta. (6th revised edn, 2008). English edn (2000) *Trust and Understanding: The person-centred approach to everyday care for people with special needs.* Ross-on-Wye: PCCS Books, (2nd revised edn, 2007).

Pörtner, M (2003) *Brücken Bauen. Menschen mit geistiger Behinderung verstehen und begleiten.* (2nd revised edn, 2007). Stuttgart: Klett-Cotta.

Pörtner, M (2005) *Alt sein ist anders. Personzentrierte Betreuung von alten Menschen,* Stuttgart: Klett-Cotta.

Prouty, G (1994) *Theoretical Evolutions in Person-Centered/Experiential Therapy: Applications to schizophrenic and retarded psychoses.* Westport, CT: Praeger.

Prouty, G (1998) Pre-therapy and the pre-expressive self. *Person-Centred Practice, 6* (2), 80–8.

Prouty, G, Van Werde, D & Pörtner, M (2002) *Pre-Therapy: Reaching contact-impaired clients.* Ross-on-Wye: PCCS Books. (Original German edition (1998) *Prä-Therapie.* Stuttgart: Klett-Cotta).

Rogers, CR (1942) *Counseling and Psychotherapy.* Boston: Houghton Mifflin.

Rogers, CR (1951) *Client-Centered Therapy: Its current practice, implications and theory.* Boston: Houghton Mifflin.

Rogers, CR (1959) A theory of therapy, personality, and interpersonal relationships, as developed in the client-centered framework. In S Koch (Ed) *Psychology: A study of a science, Vol. 3. Formulations of the person and the social context* (pp. 184–256). New York: McGraw-Hill.

Rogers, CR (1961) *On Becoming a Person.* Boston: Houghton Mifflin.

Rogers, CR (1964) Toward a modern approach to values: The valuing process in the mature person. *Journal of Abnormal and Social Psychology, 68* (2), 160–7.

Rogers, CR (1969) *Freedom to Learn.* Columbus, OH: Charles E. Merill.

Rogers, CR (1970) *On Encounter Groups.* New York: Harper & Row.

Rogers, CR (1977) *On Personal Power.* New York: Delacorte Press.

Rogers, CR (1980) *A Way of Being.* Boston: Houghton Mifflin.

Rogers, CR (1982) *Freedom to Learn for the 80s.* Boston: Houghton Mifflin.

Stierlin, H (1981) Die 'Beziehungsrealität' Schizophrener. *Psyche, 45,* 49.

Straubhaar, T (1993) Demographische Entwicklung: Problem oder Phantom? Lecture for the 50th anniversary of the Arbeitsrechtliche Vereinigung, 19 August, Hamburg.

Van Werde, D & Morton, I (1999) The relevance of Prouty's Pre-Therapy to dementia care. In I Morton, *Person-Centred Approaches to Dementia Care* (pp. 139–66). Bicester: Winslow Press.

Watzlawick, P (1976) *Wie wirklich ist die Wirklichkeit? Wahn. Täuschung. Verstehen.* München: Piper.

Index

First Steps in Counselling 3rd edn
A students' companion for basic introductory courses

Pete Sanders

ISBN 978 1 898 05951 6, £14.00

This best-selling book is used as the standard course textbook on hundreds of introductory courses throughout the UK. Each year thousands of volunteers, social workers, carers, teachers, nurses and beginning counsellors use *First Steps* as their starting point for learning.

The Person-Centred Counselling Primer

Pete Sanders

New
Primers
series

ISBN 978 1 898 05980 6, £11.00

This book presents an unparalleled, comprehensive description of person-centred counselling. Personality theory, motivation, therapy theory, non-directivity and the process of change are all covered in Pete Sanders' easy and accessible style.

The Contact Work Primer

edited by Pete Sanders

ISBN 978 1 898 05984 4, £11.00

This book introduces Pre-therapy—the work of Garry Prouty and his associates. In-patient psychiatry, clinical psychology, psychotherapy, dementia care and everyday care are covered, with contributions from Dion Van Werde, Lisbeth Sommerbeck and Penny Dodds.

Pre-Therapy

Garry Prouty, Dion Van Werde
and Marlis Pörtner

ISBN 978 1 898 05934 9, £16.00

Developed by Garry Prouty and his associates over a period of 30 years, Pre-Therapy is a method for anyone wanting to work with people whose ability to establish and maintain psychological contact is impaired temporarily or permanently, by illness or injury, whether of organic or psychological origin.

This book presents the most complete and up-to-date formulation of Pre-Therapy philosophy, theory and practice.

Applications of the method with the most difficult client groups —those described with severe psychosis and others with profound learning disabilities—are illustrated by all three authors, with detailed accounts from Dion Van Werde and Marlis Pörtner.

Pre-Therapy has changed the practice of psychologists, psychiatrists, psychotherapists, social workers, counsellors and carers in mainland Europe; now this book introduces its revolutionary ideas to English-speaking readers.

Pre-Therapy offers me a way of supporting someone at the edge of therapeutic viability and of bringing them back into therapeutic contact, in a way that is fully consistent with person-centred therapy. It is deeply respectful of the client and an effective way of making therapy available to those who might otherwise be excluded. Margaret Brown, Counselling Manager and practitioner, East Suffolk Mind, *HCPJ*, April 2003